W9-BSV-258

LITERATURE ANTHOLOGIES

A Collection of Prose and Poetry
on the Theme of

TOMORROW

Edited by
Michael Spring
Editor, Literary Cavalcade

SCHOLASTIC INC.

CURRICULUM CONSULTANTS

Ms. Jo-Ann Lynn Mullen
Associate Professor of Education
Assistant Director, Division of
Education Studies
University of Northern Colorado
Greeley, Colorado

Ms. Gaylene Pepe
Department Head, English
Colonia Senior High School
Colonia, New Jersey

STAFF

Editorial Director:	Eleanor Angeles
Project Editor:	Michael Spring
Art Director:	Joe Borzetta
Assistant Editor:	Bette Birnbaum
Contributing Consultant:	Adrienne Betz
Editorial Assistant:	Karen Salazar

COVER ART: "Ladder to the Moon," 1958, by Georgia O'Keeffe. Collection of Emily Fisher Landau. Photo by Malcolm Varon, © New York City.

ISBN 0-590-34579-6

12 11 10 9 8 7 6 5 4   9/8 0 1/9

23

ACKNOWLEDGMENTS

Grateful acknowledgment is made to the following authors and publishers for the use of copyrighted materials. Every effort has been made to obtain permission to use previously published material. Any errors or omissions are unintentional.

Isaac Asimov for "Why Read Science Fiction?" Copyright ©1985 by Isaac Asimov.
Don Congdon Associates, Inc. for "Time in Thy Flight" by Ray Bradbury. Copyright © 1953 by Ray Bradbury, renewed 1981. "Our Incredible Future" by Ray Bradbury. Copyright © 1984 by Ray Bradbury.
The Continuum Publishing Company for "Trurl's Machine" from THE CYBERIAD: Fables for the Cybernetic Age, by Stanislaw Lem. English translation copyright © 1974 by the Continuum Publishing Company.
Allan Danzig for an abridged version of "The Great Nebraska Sea."
Olga Cabral for "Electronic Tape Found in a Bottle" by Olga Cabral. Copyright © 1971 by Olga Cabral Kurtz.
Grove Press for "Prologue" from STAND UP, FRIEND, WITH ME by Edward Field. Copyright © 1963 by Edward Field.
Holt, Rinehart and Winston for "On a Tree Fallen Across the Road" from THE POETRY OF ROBERT FROST, edited by Edward Connery Lathem. Copyright 1923, © 1969 by Holt, Rinehart and Winston. Copyright 1951 by Robert Frost. "Warday," edited and abridged from the book WARDAY by Whitley Strieber and James W. Kunetka. Copyright © 1984 by Wilson & Neff, Inc. and James Kunetka.
International Creative Management, Inc. for "The Portable Phonograph" from THE WATCHFUL GODS & OTHER STORIES by Walter Van Tilburg Clark. Copyright © 1941, 1969 by Walter Van Tilburg Clark. "The Monsters Are Due on Maple Street" by Rod Serling. Copyright © 1960 by Rod Serling.
Dan Jaffe for "Forecast" by Dan Jaffe.
Little, Brown and Company for "Southbound on the Freeway" from NEW AND SELECTED THINGS TAKING PLACE by May Swenson. Copyright © 1963 by May Swenson. First appeared in *The New Yorker*. "Song of the Open Road" from VERSES FROM 1919 ON by Ogden Nash. First appeared in *The New Yorker*.
Scott Meredith Literary Agency, 845 Third Avenue, New York, NY 10022, for "Who's There" (originally "The Haunted Spacesuit") by Arthur C. Clarke. Copyright © 1958 by United Newspapers Magazine Corporation. "The King of Beasts" by Philip Jose Farmer. Copyright © 1964 by Galaxy Publishing Corporation.
William Morrow & Company, Inc. for "Predictions," excerpted from pp. 12, 14, 24, 26, 39, 70, 73, 84, 278-280, 285, 296, 396 and 401 in THE BOOK OF PREDICTIONS. Copyright © 1981 by David Wallechinsky, Amy Wallace, and Irving Wallace.
New Directions Publishing Corporation for "For the Children" from TURTLE ISLAND by Gary Snyder. Copyright © 1974 by Gary Snyder.
Alan E. Nourse for an edited version of "Image of the Gods" by Alan E. Nourse from THE COUNTERFEIT MAN. Copyright © 1963 by Alan E. Nourse.
Roberta Pryor for "Preposterous" from ANGELS AND SPACESHIPS by Fredric Brown. Copyright © 1954 by Fredric Brown.
Random House, Inc. for "The Human Family," edited and excerpted from COSMOS by Carl Sagan. Copyright © 1980 by Carl Sagan. "Harder than Granite," reprinted from THE BEGINNING AND THE END AND OTHER POEMS by Robinson Jeffers. Copyright © 1963 by Garth Jeffers and Donnan Jeffers. "The World of Tomorrow" abridged from FUTURE SHOCK, by Alvin Toffler. Copyright © 1970 by Alvin Toffler. William Faulkner's "Address Upon Receiving the Nobel Prize for Literature" from THE FAULKNER READER, copyright 1954 by William Faulkner.
Daniel J. Rogers for "Night of Lift Off 7.16.69" from STEP ON THE RAIN by Raymond Roseliep, The Rook Press, Derry, PA, 1977.
Rothco Cartoons Inc. for "The Choice" by W. Hilton-Young. © 1952 Punch/Rothco. All rights reserved.
Charles Scribner's Sons for "Earth" from THE GARDENER AND OTHER POEMS by John Hall Wheelock. Copyright © 1961 John Hall Wheelock.
Larry Sternig Literary Agency for "Terrafied" by Arthur Tofte.
Mrs. James Thurber for an edited version of "The Last Flower" by James Thurber, published by Harper & Row. Copr. © 1939 James Thurber. Copr. © 1967 Helen W. Thurber and Rosemary T. Sauers.
Warner Books, Inc. for two computer poems from THE POLICEMAN'S BEARD IS HALF CONSTRUCTED, © 1984 by William Chamberlain and Joan Hall.

ILLUSTRATION AND PHOTOGRAPHY CREDITS

Edmond Hamilton 6. Robert Burroughs 10. Frank R. Paul 12. NASA/Michael Collins 16. Jim Ludtke 18, 24, 30, 35, 38, 68, 122, 125, 150, 166, 170, 181. Greg Spalenka 44, 49, 80, 86, 90, 95, 146. Frank R. Paul 52. Brian Lewis 57. Jim Harter 60, 64, 164. Joan Hall 70. Ron Barrett 72, 77. UPI 98. Ken Hamilton 100, 108, 110, 113, 115, 132, 136, 140, 143. Werner Bischof/Magnun 120. Palomar Observatory 131. Ed Jacobus 138, 139. Jack E. Cress/Scholastic Photography Awards 153. Darryl Zudeck 154, 159.

CONTENTS

POETRY

DRAMA

"The future waits to be made and remade again."

A Letter from Ray Bradbury

OUR INCREDIBLE FUTURE

● Each of you, says Ray Bradbury, has a role to play in shaping the world of tomorrow. The future rests in your own hands.

WE FIND OURSELVES IN AMERICA PARTICIPATING in a series of continuing revolutions, all of which began in 1776. We are such a part of these turnings-over that we sometimes forget to name our good fortunes.

Thanks to the technological revolution, the average American today is richer than all the kings in history. Once only kings had horses. Now almost every family in our nation has eighty horses, combined into a single device known as an automobile.

The medical revolution has delivered us, in the main, from the terrible threat of the death of children. By the time I was eight, half my family — my brother and sister — was dead. Today, my four daughters have yet to go to their first funeral among their friends. Children still die, yes, but not in the millions that once filled the graveyards of the world.

We are part of a revolution in education. There is no longer any excuse for not being educated. All you have to do is put down this article, walk out the door, and go into the nearest library. (Remember, teachers can only inspire. All of us must finally teach ourselves.

The process must go on for a lifetime.)

Cities? Towns? Between now and the century's end we must and will rebuild all or part of every major city and most of the towns in the United States. The process is already underway. The mall, which began as a small part of our lives only twenty years ago, will grow by the thousands, offering us newer, better, safer ways of meeting people, buying goods, and seeking entertainment. We will re-find ourselves as social animals.

Need I say anything about the computer revolution? You already know what lies ahead, when it will be possible to walk around with the Encyclopedia Britannica tucked into an electronic capsule in your pocket. The ability to instantly find the fact that you want will enable you to think faster and create better.

What about space travel? THERE was an impossibility for you! When I was a boy, they said it couldn't be done, ever. When I traveled about the country as a young man, people laughed and called me Buck Rogers or Flash Gordon. I was in that terrible minority who believed in the future. I bit my tongue, and kept a list of the laughers and doubters. On the night when we landed on the Moon, I called or wrote the doubters and laughers on my list and cried, "Fools! Fools! Why didn't you believe!?"

Between now and 2001 we will begin the colonization of the Moon. You will be part of it. Just beyond — landing and colonies on Mars. You will be part of it. Solar receptors will be flung up to catch the light of the sun, beam it back to earth, and light the cities of the world. You will be part of it.

In sum, in the midst of doubts and fears and worries, you will survive, prevail, exist, and live. Your children's children will move on out through the planets, and their children in turn will move toward the stars.

All of these revolutions lie around you, circling you, changing you. You can be part of them — you can help shape them — for many of them are technological and within your reach.

This means that in the instant future of the next minute you must learn to read and write well so that you can think well about that amazing tomorrow that starts in the next hour and will continue for a hundred thousand hours or more on to the end of your life when you might well be buried in a tomato soup can between here and Alpha Centauri.

The future waits to be made and remade again. The years wait to be done up in grand packages by you.

We are all going there. I'm going with you. It will not be easy. It will often be rough. But I can't wait, can you? What a journey it will be. What a lark![1]

---

[1] **lark:** merry adventure

A CLOSER LOOK

1. List some of the continuing revolutions in America. What are some of the good things that have come from these revolutions?

2. Why does Bradbury believe that reading and writing are so important? Do you agree with him?

3. Why does Bradbury think life in the future will be better than it is today? Do you agree with him? Why or why not?

● In 1949, William Faulkner was awarded the Nobel Prize for Literature. At that time, many people were surprised that his fiction about life in the rural South had been given this honor by an international committee. Faulkner delivered one of the greatest acceptance speeches in Nobel Prize history, and his critics were silenced. In this poetic excerpt from his speech, Faulkner shows us why his ideas concern all people, regardless of the time and place in which they lived. Like most of his best work, this speech reflects Faulkner's belief in man. By "man," Faulkner means both men and women — and the unconquerable human spirit.

William Faulkner

from ADDRESS UPON RECEIVING THE NOBEL PRIZE FOR LITERATURE

I decline to accept the end of man.

It is easy enough to say that man
is immortal simply because he will endure:

     that when the last ding-dong of doom has clanged
     and faded from the last worthless rock hanging
     tideless in the last red and dying evening,

that even then there will still be one more sound:
    that of his puny
     inexhaustible[1] voice
     still
      talking.

I refuse to accept this.

I believe that man will not merely endure;
    he will prevail.[2] He is immortal,
not because he alone among the creatures has an
    inexhaustible voice,
    but because he has a soul, a spirit
capable of compassion and sacrifice and endurance.

[1] **inexhaustible:** cannot tire or be used up
[2] **prevail:** triumph

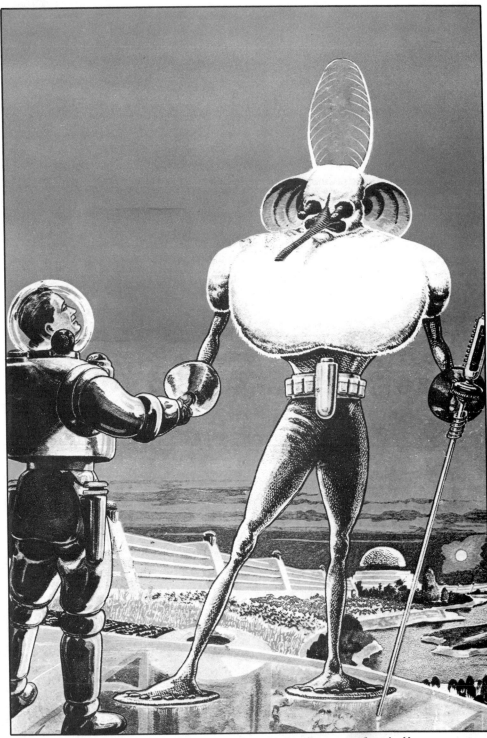

"Our age is future-oriented, the first age that is."

A Letter from Isaac Asimov

WHY READ SCIENCE FICTION?

• Science fiction is more than childish fantasy. It is an honest effort to deal with a changing world. Unlike other forms of writing, science fiction makes us look ahead and prepare for the world tomorrow.

WHY READ SCIENCE FICTION? MY OWN REASON for beginning to read it was a simple one. With its strange new worlds, monsters, inventions and dangers, it was more exciting than anything else I could find. Once I got into science fiction, everything else was pale and dull.

That's still a good reason for reading it. You won't find anything that will give you more room for stretching your mind.

But surely there must be something more to science fiction than just the fun and excitement in it. There must be, because teachers, at least in the past, sneered at it. They thought it childish and silly and refused to give it the name of literature. Now there are courses in science fiction given in almost every college, and in many high schools, too.

Why? What happened?

For one thing, people came to realize that science fiction fits this age. In fact, it is the only kind of literature that fits this age and no other, for there was no way in which it could exist until modern times.

There were, to be sure, ancient writers who told about people reaching the Moon, but these were just fantasies. They were of no more importance than fairy tales about witches and goblins, because there was no feeling in ancient times about science and what it could mean to society.

Through all of human history, there had been changes in society; new inventions, new ways of doing things. These came at such long intervals, however, and spread so slowly, that people experienced few essential changes during their lifetimes.

Everyone thought: The way things are, that's the way they'll always be.

And in that case, why write about the future?

Modern science began to develop about 1600, and its pace of progress steadily increased with the years. By 1800, the steam engine had been invented. The application of science to human affairs began to produce rapid and enormous changes. The "Industrial Revolution" took place and our way of life changed rapidly. People could see it change in the course of their lifetimes.

A brand new desire arose, one that never before existed: a yearning curiosity to know what life would be like after one was gone. What new inventions would there be? Would humans learn how to fly, how to develop ways of seeing things at a distance, or how to reach the Moon?

It wasn't till a century ago, with the Frenchman Jules Verne (1828-1905), that science fiction writers tried to deal seriously with this new desire. Science fiction became the brand new response to a brand new curiosity.

Now, a century after Jules Verne, life is changing faster than ever. When I was in high school, there were no rocket ships, no satellites, no missiles, no jet planes, no television, no air-conditioned cars, no transistors, no lasers, no organ transplants, no antibiotics, no nuclear power plants — and it hasn't been all that long since I was in high school!

Things move so quickly now that reality has started to catch up with science fiction. People who think that science fiction is "silly" look a little silly themselves. When the first atom bomb dropped, it was the people who read science fiction who weren't surprised. When the first men walked on the Moon, the suits they wore looked exactly like the drawings in science fiction stories I read when I was a boy.

These days, in fact, changes are coming so fast that we are in danger of being overwhelmed by them. Suddenly, automobiles have increased to the point where they are fouling the air. Suddenly, new plastics and new detergents are important factors in pollution. Suddenly, modern medicine cuts down the death rate the world over and we find ourselves with a population explosion.

How can we be prepared for these changes? How can we avoid being overwhelmed by unexpected disaster? Only by looking ahead and trying to foresee what might be coming.

And who have been doing this for years? Science fiction writers.

This doesn't mean that every science fiction writer foretells the future, or that every science fiction story will come true. Most science fiction deals with matters that are pure fantasy and can never come true. Nevertheless, science fiction is future-oriented. It is the only kind of literature that is; and this is important because our age is future-oriented, the first age that is.

A CLOSER LOOK

1. Why did Asimov begin to read science fiction? What reason does Asimov give to explain why science fiction is more widely read in schools today than it was in the past?

2. What does it mean to be "future-oriented"? How does a future-oriented attitude help you cope with life today?

3. Do you agree with Asimov that science fiction has not been given enough credit? Explain why you do or don't read science fiction.

• Some people are helping to create the world of tomorrow. Others stay indoors, watching life on a screen — letting life go by without them. Which type of person are you?

Dan Jaffe

THE FORECAST

Perhaps our age has driven us indoors.
We sprawl in the semi-darkness, dreaming sometimes
Of a vague world spinning in the wind.
But we have snapped our locks, pulled down our shades,
Taken all precautions. We shall not be disturbed.
If the earth shakes, it will be on a screen;
And if the prairie wind spills down our streets
And covers us with leaves, the weathermen will tell us.

"They ran and ran — what else could they do?"

Stanislaw Lem

TRURL'S MACHINE

● Computers are now a part of our daily lives. As technology advances, these "thinking machines" are becoming more and more human. Science fiction writers have always been fascinated by the idea of machines with human qualities. Why is this idea so intriguing — and so frightening?

NCE UPON A TIME TRURL THE CONSTRUCTOR built an eight-story thinking machine. When it was finished, he gave it a coat of white paint, trimmed the edges in lavender, stepped back, squinted, then added a little curlicue on the front and, where one might imagine the forehead to be, a few pale orange polka dots. Extremely pleased with himself, he whistled an air and, as is always done on such occasions, asked it the ritual question of how much is two plus two.

The machine stirred. Its tubes began to glow, its coils warmed up, current coursed through all its circuits like a waterfall, transformers hummed and throbbed. There was a clanging, and a chugging, and such a racket that Trurl began to think of adding a special muffler. Meanwhile, the machine labored on, as if it had been given the most difficult problem in the Universe to solve. The ground shook, the sand slid underfoot from the vibration, valves popped like champagne corks, the relays nearly gave way under the strain. At last, when Trurl had grown extremely impatient, the machine ground to a halt and said in a voice like thunder: "SEVEN!"

"Nonsense, my dear," said Trurl. "The answer's four. Now be a good machine and adjust yourself! What's two and two?" "Seven!" snapped the machine. Trurl sighed and put his coveralls back on, rolled up his sleeves, opened the bottom trapdoor, and crawled in. For the longest time he hammered away inside, tightened, soldered, ran clattering up and down the metal stairs, now on the sixth floor, now on the eighth. Then he pounded back down to the bottom and threw a switch, but something sizzled in the middle, and the spark plugs grew blue whiskers. After two hours of this he came out, covered with soot but satisfied. He put all his tools away, took off his coveralls, wiped his face and hands. As he was leaving, he turned and asked, just so there would be no doubt about it:

"And now what's two and two?"

"SEVEN!" replied the machine.

Trurl uttered a terrible oath, but there was no help for it — again he had to poke around inside the machine, disconnecting, correcting, checking, and resetting. When he learned for the fourth time that two and two were seven, he collapsed in despair at the foot of the machine, and sat there until Klapaucius found him. Klapaucius inquired what was wrong, for Trurl looked as if he had just returned from a funeral. Trurl explained the problem. Klapaucius crawled into the machine himself a couple of times, tried to fix this and that, then asked it for the sum of one plus two, which turned out to be six. One plus one, according to the machine, equaled zero. Klapaucius scratched his head, cleared his throat, and said:

"My friend, you'll just have to face it. That isn't the machine you wished to make. However, there's a good side to everything, including this."

"What good side?" muttered Trurl, and kicked the base on which he was sitting.

"Stop that," said the machine.

"H'm, it's sensitive, too. But where was I? Oh yes, there's no question but that we have here a stupid machine. And not merely stupid in the usual, normal way, oh no! This is, as far as I can determine — and you know I am something of an expert — this is the stupidest thinking machine in the entire world, and that's nothing to sneeze at! To construct deliberately such a machine would be far from easy; in fact, I would say that no one could manage it. For the thing is not only stupid, but stubborn as a mule."

"What earthly use do I have for such a machine?!" said Trurl, and kicked it again.

"I'm warning you, you better stop!" said the machine.

"A warning, if you please," observed Klapaucius dryly. "Not only is it sensitive, dense, and stubborn, but quick to take offense. Believe me, with such an abundance of qualities there are all sorts of things you might do!"

"What, for example?" asked Trurl.

"Well, it's hard to say offhand. You might put it on exhibit and charge admission. People would flock to see the stupidest thinking machine that ever was — what does it have, eight stories? Really, could anyone imagine a bigger dunce? And the exhibition would not only cover your costs, but — "

"Enough, I'm not holding an exhibition!" Trurl said. He stood up and, unable to restrain himself, kicked the machine once more.

"This is your third warning," said the machine.

"What?" cried Trurl, infuriated by its imperious[1] manner. "You . . . you . . . " And he kicked it several times, shouting: "You're only good for kicking, you know that?"

"You have insulted me for the fourth, fifth, sixth, and eighth times," said the machine. "Therefore I refuse to answer all further questions of a mathematical nature."

"It refuses! Do you hear that?" fumed Trurl, thoroughly exasperated. "After six comes eight — did you notice, Klapaucius? — not seven, but eight! And *that's* the kind of mathematics Her Highness refuses to perform! Take that! And that! And that! Or perhaps you'd like some more?"

The machine shuddered, shook, and without another word started to lift itself from its foundations. They were very deep, and the girders began to bend. But at last it scrambled out, leaving behind broken concrete blocks with steel spokes protruding — and it bore down on Trurl and Klapaucius like a moving fortress. Trurl was so dumbfounded that he didn't even try to hide from the machine, which to all appearances intended to crush him to a pulp. But Klapaucius grabbed his arm and yanked him away, and the two of them took to their heels. When finally they looked back, they saw the machine swaying like a high tower, advancing slowly, at every step sinking to its second floor, but stubbornly, doggedly pulling itself out of the sand and heading straight for them.

"Whoever heard of such a thing?" Trurl gasped in amazement.

"Why, this is mutiny! What do we do now?"

"Wait and watch," replied the prudent[2] Klapaucius. "We may learn something."

But there was nothing to be learned just then. The machine had reached firmer ground and was picking up speed. Inside, it whistled, hissed, and sputtered.

"Any minute now the signal box will knock loose," said Trurl under his breath. "That'll jam the program and stop it."

"No," said Klapaucius, "this is a special case. The thing is so stupid, that even if the whole transmission goes, it won't matter. But — look out!"

The machine was gathering speed, clearly bent on running them down. They fled just as fast as they could, the fearful rhythm of crunching steps in their ears. They ran and ran — what else could they do? They tried to make it back to their native district, but the machine outflanked them, cut them off, forced them deeper and deeper into a wild, uninhabited region. Mountains, dismal and craggy, slowly rose out of the mist. Trurl, panting heavily, shouted to Klapaucius:

"Listen! Let's turn into some narrow canyon . . . where it won't be able to follow us . . . the cursed thing. What do you say?"

"No, better go straight," wheezed Klapaucius. "There's a town up ahead . . . can't remember the name. Anyway, we can find — shelter there."

So they ran straight and soon saw houses before them. The streets were practically deserted at this time of day, and the constructors had gone a good distance without meeting a living soul, when suddenly an awful crash, like an avalanche at the edge of the town, indicated that the machine was coming after them.

Trurl looked back and groaned.

"Good heavens! It's tearing down the houses, Klapaucius!!"

The machine, in stubborn pursuit, was plowing through the walls of the buildings like a mountain of steel. In its wake lay piles of rubble and white clouds of plaster dust. There were dreadful screams, and confusion in the streets. Trurl and Klapaucius, their hearts in their mouths, ran on till they came to a large town hall. They darted inside and raced down endless stairs to a deep cellar.

"It won't get us in here, even if it brings the whole building down on our heads!" panted Klapaucius. "But really, the devil himself had me pay you a visit today. I was curious to see how your work was going — well, I certainly found out."

And indeed, the cellar opened up and the mayor entered, accompanied by several aldermen.[3] Trurl was too embarrassed to explain how this strange and disastrous situation had come about; Klapaucius had to do it. The mayor listened in silence. Suddenly the walls trembled, the ground heaved, and the sound of cracking stone reached them in the cellar.

"It's here?!" cried Trurl.

"Yes," said the mayor. "And it demands that we give you up, otherwise it says it will level the entire town."

Just then they heard, far overhead, words that honked as if from a muffled horn:

"Trurl's here . . . I smell Trurl."

"But surely you won't give us up?"

"The one of you who calls himself Trurl must leave. The other may remain, since surrendering him does not constitute part of the conditions."

"Have mercy!"

"We are helpless," said the mayor. "And were you to stay here, Trurl, you would have to answer for all the damage done to this town and its inhabitants, since it was because of you that the machine destroyed sixteen homes and buried beneath their ruins many of our finest citizens. Only the fact that you yourself stand in imminent[4] peril permits me to let you leave unpunished. Go then, and nevermore return."

Trurl looked at the aldermen and, seeing his sentence written on their stern faces, slowly turned and made for the door.

"Wait! I'll go with you!" cried Klapaucius impulsively.

"You?" said Trurl, a faint hope in his voice. "But no . . . " he added after a moment. "Why should you have to perish, too?"

"Nonsense!" replied Klapaucius with great energy. "What, us perish at the hands of that iron imbecile? Never! It takes more than that, my friend, to wipe two of the most famous constructors off the face of the globe! Come, Trurl! Chin up!"

Encouraged by these words, Trurl ran up the stairs after Klapaucius. There was not a soul outside in the square. Amid clouds of dust and the skeletons of destroyed homes, stood the machine, higher than the town hall tower itself, puffing steam, covered with the blood of powdered brick and smeared with chalk.

23

"What do you think it's waiting for now?"

"Careful!" whispered Klapaucius. "It doesn't see us. Let's take that first street on the left, then turn right, then straight for those mountains. There we can hide and think of how to make the thing give up once and for all its insane . . . *Now!*" he yelled, for the machine had just spotted them and was charging, making the pavement buckle.

Breathless, they ran from the town and galloped along for a mile or so. They heard behind them the thunderous stride of the colossus.[5]

"I know that ravine!" Klapaucius suddenly cried. "That's the bed of a dried-out stream and it leads to cliffs and caves — faster, faster, the thing'll have to stop soon!"

So they raced uphill, stumbling and waving their arms to keep their balance, but the machine still gained on them. Scrambling up over the gravel of the dried-out riverbed, they reached a crevice in the perpendicular rock. They saw high above them the murky mouth of a cave, and began to climb frantically toward it, no longer caring about the loose stones that flew from under their feet. The opening in the rock breathed chill and darkness. As quickly as they could, they leaped inside, ran a few extra steps, then stopped.

"Well, here at least we're safe," said Trurl, calm once again. "I'll just take a look, to see where it got stuck."

"Be careful," cautioned Klapaucius. Trurl inched his way to the edge of the cave, leaned out, and immediately jumped back in fright.

"It's coming up the mountain!" he cried.

"Don't worry, it'll never be able to get in here," said Klapaucius, not altogether convinced. "But what's that? Is it getting dark? Oh no!"

At that moment a great shadow blotted out the bit of sky visible through the mouth of the cave. In its place appeared a smooth steel wall with rows of rivets. It was the machine slowly sealing up the cave with a rock, as if with a mighty metal lid.

"We're trapped . . . " whispered Trurl, his voice breaking off when the darkness became absolute.

"That was idiotic on our part!" Klapaucius exclaimed, furious. "To jump into a cave that it could barricade! How could we have done such a thing?"

"What do you think it's waiting for now?" asked Trurl after a long pause.

"For us to give up — that doesn't take any great brains."

Again there was silence. Trurl tiptoed in the darkness, hands outstretched, in the direction of the opening. He ran his fingers along the stone until he touched the smooth steel, which was warm, as if heated from within.

"I feel Trurl . . . " boomed the iron voice. Trurl hastily retreated, and took a seat alongside his friend. For some time they sat there, motionless. At last Klapaucius whispered:

"There's no sense our just sitting here. I'll try to reason with it."

"That's hopeless," said Trurl. "But go ahead; perhaps it will at least let you go free."

"Now, now, none of that!" said Klapaucius, patting him on the back. And he groped his way toward the mouth of the cave and called: "Hello out there, can you hear us?"

"Yes," said the machine.

"Listen, we'd like to apologize. You see . . . well, there was a little misunderstanding, true, but it was nothing, really. Trurl had no intention of . . . "

"I'll pulverize[6] Trurl!" said the machine. "But first he'll tell me how much two and two makes."

"Of course he will, of course he will, and you'll be happy with his answer, and make it up with him for sure, isn't that right, Trurl?" said the mediator soothingly.

"Yes, of course," mumbled Trurl.

"Really?" said the machine. "Then how much is two and two?"

"Fo . . . that is, seven . . . " said Trurl in an even lower voice.

"Ha! Not four, but seven, eh?" crowed the machine. "There, I told you so!"

"Seven, yes, seven, we always knew it was seven!" Klapaucius eagerly agreed. "Now will you, uh, let us go?" he added cautiously.

"No. Let Trurl say how sorry he is and tell me how much is two times two."

"And you'll let us go, if I do?" asked Trurl.

"I don't know. I'll think about it. I'm not making any deals. What's two times two?"

"But you probably will let us go, won't you?" said Trurl, while Klapaucius pulled on his arm and hissed in his ear: "The thing's an imbecile, don't argue with it, for heaven's sake!"

"I won't let you go, if I don't want to," said the machine. "You just tell me how much two times two is."

Suddenly Trurl fell into a rage.

"I'll tell you, I'll tell you all right!" he screamed. "Two and two is four and two times two is four, even if you stand on your head, pound these mountains all to dust, drink the ocean dry, and swallow the sky — do you hear? Two and two is four!!"

"Trurl! What are you saying? Have you taken leave of your senses? Two and two is seven, nice machine! Seven, seven!!" howled Klapaucius, trying to drown out his friend.

"No! It's four! Four and only four, four from the beginning to the end of time — FOUR!!" bellowed Trurl, growing hoarse.

The rock beneath their feet was seized with a feverish tremor.

The machine moved away from the cave, letting in a little pale light, and gave a piercing scream:

"That's not true. It's seven! Say it's seven or I'll hit you!"

"Never!" roared Trurl, as if he no longer cared what happened. Pebbles and dirt rained down on their heads, for the machine had begun to ram its eight-story hulk again and again into the wall of stone. It hurled itself against the mountainside until huge boulders broke away and went tumbling down into the valley.

Thunder and sulfurous fumes filled the cave. Sparks flew from the blows of steel on rock, yet one could still make out, now and then, the ragged voice of Trurl bawling:

"Two and two is four! Two and two is four!!"

Klapaucius attempted to shut his friend's mouth by force. But, violently thrown off, he gave up, sat and covered his head with his arms. Not for a moment did the machine's mad efforts flag. It seemed that any minute now the ceiling would collapse, crush the prisoners, and bury them forever. But when they had lost all hope, and the air was thick with acrid smoke and choking dust, there was suddenly a horrible scraping, and a sound like a slow explosion, louder than all the maniacal banging and battering. The air whooshed, and the black wall that blocked the cave was whisked away, as if by a hurricane. Monstrous chunks of rock came crushing down after it. The echoes of that avalanche still rumbled and reverberated[7] in the valley below when the two friends peered out of their cave. They saw the machine. It lay smashed and flattened,

27

nearly broken in half by an enormous boulder that had landed in the middle of its eight floors. With the greatest care they picked their way down through the smoking rubble. In order to reach the river-bed, it was necessary to pass the remains of the machine, which resembled the wreck of some mighty vessel thrown up upon a beach. Without a word, the two stopped together in the shadow of its twisted hull. The machine still quivered slightly, and one could hear something turning, creaking feebly, within.

"Yes, this is the bad end you've come to, and two and two is — as it always was — " began Trurl, but just then the machine made a faint, barely audible croaking noise and said, for the last time, "SEVEN!"

Then something snapped inside. A few stones dribbled down from overhead, and now before them lay nothing but a lifeless mass of scrap. The two constructors exchanged a look and silently, without any further comment or conversation, walked back the way they came.

[1] **imperious:** arrogant; commanding
[2] **prudent:** cautious
[3] **aldermen:** officers of a city
[4] **imminent:** immediate; about to happen
[5] **colossus:** resembling a gigantic statue
[6] **pulverize:** crush into small pieces
[7] **reverberated:** echoed

A CLOSER LOOK

1. What was wrong with the machine Trurl built? Why does Klapaucius think Trurl should put this machine on exhibit?

2. In what ways is the machine like a human being? In what ways is it not like a human being?

3. Compare the personalities of Trurl and Klapaucius. Would you, like Trurl, have insisted that two and two are four? Or would you, like Klapaucius, have said that two and two are seven in order to save your life? Explain your answer.

• Problems may be difficult to deal with, but they do encourage you to think, and they do force you to take action. Whatever your problems — Frost seems to be saying — they usually don't last terribly long, and they're not likely to stop you from reaching your goals.

Robert Frost

ON A TREE FALLEN ACROSS THE ROAD
(To hear us talk)

The tree the tempest with a crash of wood
Throws down in front of us is not to bar
Our passage to our journey's end for good,
But just to ask us who we think we are

Insisting always on our own way so.
She likes to halt us in our runner tracks,
And make us get down in a foot of snow
Debating what to do without an ax.

And yet she knows obstruction is in vain:
We will not be put off the final goal
We have it hidden in us to attain,
Not though we have to seize earth by the pole

And, tired of aimless circling in one place,
Steer straight off after something into space.

29

"You don't like Terra, do you?"

Arthur Tofte

Terrafied

● Science fiction writers often try to warn us about the dangers of technology. These writers are critical only because they care so much about the quality of life. They want us to see where we're going wrong, so that we can learn the truth about ourselves and mend our ways. The planet that Dor visits is a future version of the Earth we know today. Look through her eyes as she sees Earth, or Terra, for the first time.

OR PEERED UP AT THE STRANGE OBJECT IN THE deep blue sky. It seemed very small and very far away. Yet, even as she watched, it grew steadily larger and larger. Never before had she seen anything in the sky. There were no flying creatures on the planet Tyrox.

Her clawlike hands pulled back on the slender leather reins that controlled her throll. Today was Dor's fourteenth birthday. The throll was her parents' birthday gift. It was a beautiful six-legged beast, fully twenty feet long from its single horn to its six-foot tail. Best of all, it was full of spirit and swift as the wind. Not yet fully grown, it would be her personal mount for years to come.

Dor watched as the flying object sped downward toward her. Whatever it was, Dor knew it was not from Tyrox.

Dor pulled the throll around and headed back to her village. It would be wise to return home quickly and warn the others. But before the throll had taken a dozen steps, the flying object settled down directly in her path. Flames were shooting from beneath it as it slowly came to rest.

31

Terror-stricken by the flames, the throll leaped sideways in a forty-foot jump that unseated his young rider. Dor landed on the thick turf with a jolt that knocked her unconscious.

When she opened her three eyes, she had trouble focusing them. It seemed that a tall, very pale-skinned creature was standing over her. She felt short, stubby fingers probing her for injuries. Apparently it was a thinking animal. Only a thinking animal would do that.

Dor sat up. The creature was taller by a foot than anyone in her village. He was dressed in a tight-fitting, one-piece uniform made of a shiny, metallic substance. But what shocked Dor more than anything else was that the creature had only two eyes. That, and two rows of deadly teeth, which she saw whenever he smiled.

Dor sensed that the smile was to reassure her. But she was not reassured. She was terrified.

When Dor tried to stand, she winced with pain. One of her ankles had been twisted. She took a half-step, and fell back to the ground.

The tall creature reached down, picked her up, and carried her up a short ladder into the space craft. She was placed in a sleeping pod, and tied down with straps. Then she felt a stab in her arm.

When she awoke hours later, the tall stranger was looking down at her. Again he was smiling.

The craft, Dor realized, had taken off from Tyrox. She was allowed to get out of her sleeping pod and take a few tentative steps. Her hurt ankle had been wrapped with bindings, and she could stand on it now.

There were four creatures on the ship, each with two eyes and ferocious-looking teeth. They seemed friendly enough, though. They tried to speak to her, but she understood nothing. After she had eaten, she was taken to a control room where, on a giant screen, a green sphere appeared. It was her own planet, thousands of miles away. "Tyrox!" she cried. It was the first word she had uttered which these creatures understood.

Later, lying in her pod, Dor thought of the terrible situation she was in. What was going to happen to her? Who were these two-eyed strangers? Where did they come from? What would her mother and father think when the throll returned without her?

She tried not to panic. Her only chance, she knew, was to keep her wits about her. She would learn everything she could about the ship and its crew. By biding her time, she might have a chance.

What she mustn't do is lose her courage.

The next day, the crew began teaching Dor their language. She learned that they called themselves human beings, and that they were from the third planet in a small solar system, a planet called Terra. The captain's name was Cahorn.

As the days passed into weeks and into months, Dor learned to speak the Terran language fluently. Captain Cahorn tried to learn the Tyroxan language, but Dor did her best to be a poor teacher. If she was going to escape, it was important that she learn everything about her captors, and that they learn as little as possible about her.

In many ways Dor felt brighter, sharper than the four men on the ship. She watched them at their work, and studied the ship's controls until she had mastered them. She was especially interested in the long-range communications system which kept the men in contact with their home planet. It was similar to the system in use on Tyrox for centuries. Dor saw it as her only hope for communicating with Tyrox — if only she could get to the controls alone.

Dor told her captors about the beauty of Tyrox; about its deep blue skies and rolling green hills; its clear, fresh water abounding with fish. Waterfalls, she explained, gave them hydroelectric power, and mountain ranges provided them with all the minerals they would ever need. The birth rate equalled the death rate, so the population always remained the same. People lived in villages spaced far apart, and conflicts between the villages were unheard of.

Dor had her own questions to ask. What was Terra like? Why had they taken her prisoner? What were they going to do with her? Would she ever be able to go home?

Captain Cahorn had grown fond of Dor in the months they had spent together, speeding back to Terra. "We had reports of a habitable planet in your solar system," he explained. "Our mission was to check it out. We were to try, if possible, to bring a native of your planet back to our head office on Terra."

"But why me?" Dor asked.

"It was just chance, I'm afraid. You were thrown from your horse and — "

"What's going to happen to me now?"

Captain Cahorn patted Dor's arm. "We're amazed at how quickly you picked up our language," he said. "By Terra standards, you're quite a genius. I can't tell you everything now — only that you and your people may be able to save us all — "

"What is it really like on Terra?"

Captain Cahorn shrugged his shoulders. "Terra, or Earth as it's sometimes called, has a bit of everything. It has wide oceans and great stretches of sandy desert. It has mountains and valleys — and even a few forests. There's ice and snow at both poles, and a few jungles near the equator. But most of Terra is filled with vast cities that cover hundreds of square miles."

"Are the people of Terra happy?"

"Some are, many are not."

"Why not?"

"A variety of reasons. Some nations are very poor. Some have too many people with not enough to eat. Some are always at war."

"War? What's that?"

"That's when people can't get along with each other. Hundreds of thousands of people die from war each year. But you needn't concern yourself with this. Where I'm taking you is very peaceful. We are so strong that no one dares attack us."

"And where is that?"

"Dor, I've been in contact with headquarters. It's going to take the computers a few days to analyze your statements — the things you've told us about Tyrox. In the meantime, you're going to come and stay with me. You'll have privacy there. It will also give you a chance to see how we live. I have a son just about your age. And a daughter a year younger. You'll like them."

Dor turned away. "But will they like me? With my three eyes? My blue skin? I haven't teeth like yours, or hands. My head is larger than yours, and my body is smaller."

"I don't blame you for worrying — "

"Could I ask a favor?"

"If it's anything I can do — "

"Could I tell my father and mother where I am?"

Captain Cahorn looked at her with surprise. "How could you do that?"

"I've studied your long-range communications system. If you'd follow the instructions which I've written down — "

Captain Cahorn took the slip of paper and smiled at Dor with a new-found respect.

Two days later the ship landed at a high-security spaceport. Captain Cahorn hustled Dor across the landing field to a waiting ski

"Terra . . . has a bit of everything."

taxi. Three hours later they were standing together in the captain's suburban home. The fifth-floor apartment was part of a building complex covering five square miles. Each apartment had a plastic-enclosed balcony where vines and ferns were allowed to grow. Only someone as important as the captain could afford to live there.

Captain Cahorn's family had entertained people from outer space before, so they were not particularly shocked by Dor's appearance. The captain's thirteen-year-old daughter, Renna, was flustered, however. Those three eyes of Dor's seemed to look right through her.

Bob, the captain's tall, sixteen-year-old son had no compunction[1] about stepping forward and taking Dor's clawlike hand.

"Welcome to Terra," he said. "You'll be staying in Renna's room. There's a football game on now; if you'd like to watch — "

Dor shook her head. "I don't know what football is."

"Come, I'll show you."

A few minutes later, Dor, Renna, and Bob were seated in front of a three-dimensional vistascope screen, watching men line up and hurl themselves at each other, either carrying, throwing, or kicking an oval ball. It was more violence than Dor had ever seen in her life.

35

"Is this what you call war?" she asked.

Renna laughed. "No. It's just a game."

"Don't they get hurt?"

"Sure," Bob said. "Quite often. But football players are paid to take their chances."

"Paid?" Dor asked. "You mean they're given more food than others?"

Bob looked at her with wonder. "You mean you don't know what pay is? Oh, boy! What a lot you have to learn!"

While the computers digested information about Dor's planet, the captain and his family remained on strict orders to keep Dor happy, occupied, and out of the public eye.

The next morning Dor was dressed in Terra clothes and taken by Bob on a drive through the city. The tinted-glass windows kept busybodies from looking in at his unusual guest from outer space.

"You're lucky you didn't come to Terra last year," Bob said, as he started up his small electric car. "The smog was terrible. We saw the sun only eight times all year. Things are better now; we've been able to see the sun at least three times every month."

"Smog? What's that?"

"Look around, Dor. What you see in the air is smog. It's made from smoke and fog and all kinds of polluting gases."

"What caused it?"

"A lot of it came in the old days from gasoline-burning cars, coal-burning power plants, mills, and factories. That's all been changed. But they say it may take another hundred years to get the air clean again."

"Why isn't something being done?"

"Oh, it is. We're spending billions of dollars to clean the air. But we let it go too long."

"And your oceans and lakes and rivers," Dor exclaimed, "how about them?"

Bob grimaced. "I guess we've just about given up on them. About all we can do is purify the water we use for drinking and bathing."

"Where do you get your fish?"

"We don't. My father told me that when he was a small boy his father took him fishing and he actually caught a fish. As far as I know, all the fish on the planet today are in public aquariums. The oceans haven't had any fish in them for nearly half a century.''

Bob turned to Dor. ''Enough of this serious talk. There isn't much to see in this city — just buildings. Let's have some excitement. I don't get many chances to drive; let's go for a short ride on one of our old superhighways. It's in terrible shape now and no one uses it, but there's a section about fifteen miles long where the guys go — *when* they can get their family cars. It's where we find out how fast we can go. And who has the most nerve.''

Bob laughed with pleasure as he slapped the gas pedal to the floor and headed up a ramp. ''Hold on,'' he cried, ''here we go!''

Dor held tightly to her seat belt as the car sped along the deserted highway.

''The trick,'' Bob said, ''is to avoid the potholes. You hit one of them at high speed and you're through.''

Dor watched with horror as Bob sent the car plunging ahead. ''Must we go so fast?'' she cried out. ''Riding my throll was nothing like this!''

''Don't worry, Dor, I'll be careful. Oh, look, there's an old steam car. Let's try to pass it. Hold on! Here we come!''

The car leaped forward. A moment later they were alongside the steam car. Bob gave its driver a derisive[2] wave as though challenging him to a race.

Not to be outdone, the other driver increased his speed. Soon the two cars, side by side, were screaming along the wide freeway.

Dor saw it first — a third, slower car ahead of them, weaving back and forth to avoid a series of dangerous potholes. Almost at the same moment Bob saw it. He slammed on the brakes and skidded sideways.

In the smog, the driver of the steam car did not see the danger until too late. Dor watched with horror as the steam car, trying to avoid Bob, smashed first against the metal guardrails, then into the slower car in front. There was a series of violent crushing noises as the two cars smashed into each other. Both were complete wrecks.

Bob, in the meantime, was able to get his car under control. With skill, he slid past the two tangled cars and continued on his way.

''Whew!'' he said, ''that was close. Wait until I tell the guys at school about this. Will they be jealous!''

''You mean you do this for fun?'' Dor asked.

''Sure it's fun. Of course, the idea is to get involved without getting hurt.''

"What was going to happen to her?"

"How can you avoid getting hurt? Those two drivers back there — shouldn't we go back and help them? They might be badly hurt."

"Go back?" Bob was genuinely surprised. "No one ever goes back on the freeway. It would be sure suicide."

He pointed ahead. "That's where the good section ends. It's mostly rubble ahead. When we get down this ramp, you'll be able to see the city."

Dor looked about. Both sides of the street were lined with towering buildings, all alike. The top floors were lost in smog. Traffic crawled along, bumper to bumper. The narrow sidewalks were almost empty.

Dor finally spoke. "I'd like to go back to your home now. I'm frightened."

"Aw, you'll get used to it."

As they inched along in the heavy traffic, Dor said, "I don't understand. Why don't you do something about conditions on Terra — clean it up?"

"We're doing everything we can. But as I said, we let it go too long."

He turned to Dor. "That's where you come in."

"Me? What can I do about it?"

Bob peered over at his companion. "Perhaps I shouldn't be telling you about this, Dor. But I heard my father talking to his boss last night. He said that, according to the computer reports, Tyrox would be a wonderful place for people from Terra to settle and colonize. He said it would easily support a billion of our overpopulation."

"You mean the people from this planet would go to my planet and take over?"

"Oh, I'm sure we'd pay you well for it."

"Pay us — how? With pollution of our air and water? And what can you give us in payment? Surely you don't think we would want the kind of life you have here?"

"Oh, I don't know. We can give you the benefit of our advanced technology. That's worth a great deal."

Dor turned her face away. Her heart was heavy.

Captain Cahorn greeted them when they returned home. "I've got good news for you, Dor," he said. "You were right about the communications system."

"You've been able to contact my father?"

"Yes, we have. We've made contact with Tyrox. I've always felt badly that I took you away from your parents; I'm glad to help make amends now."

"When can I talk with my father?"

"As soon as everything is set up. The conversation will be relayed over the entire intercontinental vistascope network. People all over the world will be able to see you and hear you talk with your father. You'll be quite a celebrity, Dor."

"But I'll be speaking in Tyroxan."

"After you've talked to your father you can translate what both of you have said into Terran language. The vistascope people are setting up their equipment in our family room. Why don't you wait in Renna's room? It's the only quiet place left."

Renna was lying on her bed, reading, when Dor entered. The two girls looked warily at each other. Suddenly Renna's face broke into a broad smile.

"You don't like Terra, do you?" she asked softly. Her blue eyes were clear and innocent, yet intelligent.

Dor grinned. "It's different," she managed to say in reply.

"From what Father has told us, Tyrox is a beautiful place."

"It is," Dor nodded.

Renna shook her head. "You know what they're planning to do, don't you?"

"Bob told me this morning. Terra would like to colonize Tyrox."

"Do you realize what that means?"

"I can guess."

"It's impossible for you to guess," Renna said. "You haven't seen enough of what life is like on our planet. Billions of people will be listening to your talk today. As you talk, they'll be envisioning Tyrox — the green fields, the pure streams, the clean air. To them it will be the dream of Terra as it once was . . . the dream your planet now suddenly makes real to them."

The Earth girl sat down on the edge of her bed and buried her head in her hands.

"I like you, Dor. There's nothing I would like better than to leave Terra and go to Tyrox. But it's too cruel."

"What do you mean — cruel?"

Renna looked up at her. "We here on Terra are doomed. We know it. We've polluted not only our air and water, we've polluted our minds and characters as well. With our billions of people crowded together, life has become a raging struggle for survival. It's like a disease, a plague. That's what our people would bring to Tyrox. And there's nothing you can do to stop it."

"Are you suggesting that I try?"

Renna shook her head. "The company my father works for spent billions on the exploratory expedition to Tyrox. It's by far the most suitable planet discovered so far. They've even started selling one-way tickets. I might add that as a reward to my father, the entire Cahorn family is scheduled for an early departure. Not as early as yours, of course."

"Mine? I'm being sent back to Tyrox?" Dor cried out in eagerness.

"Yes, my young friend," Captain Cahorn said from the open doorway. "I convinced my company that it was good protection to have you along on the first ship. It leaves next week, and will carry some of our leading biologists, chemists, geologists, communicators, and, of course, the military. It will be their job to analyze all phases of life on Tyrox and prepare the way for the colonists to come. You'll get to see your parents again, and we'll be guaranteed a fair reception. You'll get paid, of course, to serve as our interpreter.''

He paused, a worried look on his face. "But come, Dor, the vistascope people are ready for you. The whole world is tuned in to see and hear you. I know you're anxious to talk to your father and tell him you're among friends. Just reassure him that all's well with you. Later, when our plans are more definite, we can tell him when he can expect your return.''

In the family room, Dor was almost blinded by the strong lights. She was seated in the center, surrounded by technicians. Several vistascope cameras were leveled at her. Over to one side she could see Renna and Bob with their mother.

"As soon as you can hear your father's voice, you can begin talking,'' Cahorn told her.

For a moment or two, Dor waited in silence, listening for her father's voice. When it came through, amplified, as clear as if he were in the same room, Dor had difficulty holding back a sigh of relief.

Then she spoke, very slowly and carefully, in the graceful, lilting Tyroxan tongue.

"Father,'' she said, "I am a prisoner on a planet called Terra.

"The people here are desperate. I feel sorry for them. There are billions and billions of them. Everything is polluted. They are looking for other planets to colonize to relieve the horrible pressure.

"Yes, Father, they want to send many of their people to Tyrox, at least a billion. But as I love you and you love me, don't let even that first ship land.

"They are sending a ship next week with some of their top scientists. You must prevent it from landing. You have not yet three hundred Tyroxan days to prepare your defenses. I recall hearing that special machinery for laser disintegrators and magnetic shields were developed a century ago when we thought we were in danger from another invader. Use those three hundred days to reactivate the shields and the disintegrators.

"No, Father, all Terrans are not evil. They are like people caught in a deadly plague. They are frightened. The people I am living with are very kind to me. I wish we could help them. But it's only common sense to refuse to admit the plague. If they are unable to land on Tyrox, it will force them to search further for other habitable planets, preferably unpopulated. Tyrox must be saved!

"No, Father, they do not understand what I am saying to you. I know their language. They do not know ours.

"Tell Mother and all my friends that I am well treated. I admit I am frightened. Perhaps I should say I am *Terra*fied . . . terrified of what Terra could do to Tyrox. Don't let that first ship land, Father."

Dor raised her three eyes, glistening with half-shed tears, and looked up at Captain Cahorn.

"And now could you tell us what you told your father?" the spaceman asked.

Dor nodded. "I told him that life is quite different here than it is on Tyrox. I told him that I was well and that I was being very well treated."

"Did you tell your father that you were going to be on the first ship to go to Tyrox? I'm anxious that we are favorably welcomed."

Dor looked back at the Terran spaceman. "No," she said with the half-smile of a secret unshared. "I didn't say anything about my being on that first ship. I did tell him, however, how to welcome it."

[1] **compunction:** anxiety; distress
[2] **derisive:** scornful

A CLOSER LOOK

1. How would you describe life on Tyrox? How is life on Tyrox different from life on Terra?

2. What is Dor's opinion of Terra? What opinion would she have of Earth if she visited today? What would you want to tell her about our planet?

3. What does Dor ask her father to do? Do you think her decision is wise? Why or why not?

● Joyce Kilmer's famous poem "Trees" begins with the line, "I think that I shall never see a poem as lovely as a tree." In Nash's lighthearted poem, Kilmer's nature-loving statement is updated to suit a modern environment.

Ogden Nash

Song of the Open Road

I think that I shall never see
A billboard lovely as a tree.
Indeed, unless the billboards fall
I'll never see a tree at all.

"So that was a circus."

44

Ray Bradbury
TIME IN THY FLIGHT

● If you could go back in time, would you see the same world you
read about in history books? Janet, William, and Robert are children
of the future looking back upon our civilization. Their impression of
our "primitive" culture is not exactly what their teacher expected.
After reading Bradbury's story, you'll understand why he's called a
man of the future whose heart is in the past.

THE WIND BLEW THE LONG YEARS AWAY PAST
their hot faces. The Time Machine stopped. "Nineteen
hundred and twenty-eight," said Janet. The two boys
looked past her.

Mr. Fields stirred. "Remember, you're here to observe the behavior of these ancient people. Be inquisitive,[1] be intelligent, observe."

"Yes," said the girl and the two boys in crisp khaki uniforms.
They wore identical haircuts, had identical wristwatches, sandals,
and coloring of hair, eyes, teeth, and skin, though they were not
related.

"Shh!" said Mr. Fields.

They looked out at a little Illinois town in the spring of the year.
A cool mist lay on the early morning streets.

Far down the street a small boy came running in the last light of
the marble-cream moon. Somewhere a great clock struck 5 a.m. far
away. Leaving tennis-shoe prints softly in the quiet lawns, the boy
stepped near the invisible Time Machine and cried up to a high,
dark, house window.

The house window opened. Another boy crept down the roof to the ground. The two boys ran off with banana-filled mouths into the dark, cold morning.

"Follow them," whispered Mr. Fields. "Study their life patterns. Quick!"

Janet and William and Robert ran on the cold pavements of spring, visible now, through the slumbering town, through a park. All about, lights flickered, doors clicked, and other children rushed alone or in gasping pairs down a hill to some gleaming blue tracks.

"Here it comes!" The children milled about before dawn. Far down the shining tracks a small light grew seconds later into steaming thunder.

"What is it?" screamed Janet.

"A train, silly. You've seen pictures of them!" shouted Robert.

And as the Time Children watched, from the train stepped gigantic gray elephants, steaming the pavements with their mighty waters, lifting question-mark nozzles to the cold morning sky. Cumbrous[2] wagons rolled from the long freight flats, red and gold. Lions roared and paced in boxed darkness.

"Why — *this* must be a — circus!" Janet trembled.

"You think so? Whatever happened to them?"

"Like Christmas, I guess. Just vanished, long ago."

Janet looked around. "Oh, it's awful, isn't it?"

The boys stood numbed. "It sure is."

Men shouted in the faint gleam of dawn. Sleeping cars drew up, dazed faces blinked out at the children. Horses clattered like a great fall of stones on the pavement.

Mr. Fields was suddenly behind the children. "Disgusting, barbaric, keeping animals in cages. If I'd known this was here, I'd never have let you come see. This is a terrible ritual."

"Oh, yes." But Janet's eyes were puzzled. "And yet, you know, it's like a nest of maggots. I want to study it."

"I don't know," said Robert, his eyes darting, his fingers trembling. "It's pretty crazy. We might try writing a thesis on it if Mr. Fields says it's all right ."

Mr. Fields nodded. "I'm glad you're digging in here, finding motives, studying this horror. All right — we'll see the circus this afternoon."

"I think I'm going to be sick," said Janet.

The Time Machine hummed.

"So that was a circus," said Janet, solemnly.

The trombone circus died in their ears. The last thing they saw was candy-pink trapeze people whirling while baking powder clowns shrieked and bounded.

"You must admit psychovision's better," said Robert slowly.

"All those nasty animal smells, the excitement." Janet blinked. "That's bad for children, isn't it? And those older people seated with the children. Mothers, fathers, they called them. Oh, that *was* strange."

Mr. Fields put some marks in his class grading book.

Janet shook her head numbly. "I want to see it all again. I've missed the motives somewhere. I want to make that run across town again in the early morning. The cold air on my face — the sidewalk under my feet — the circus train coming in. Was it the air and the early hour that made the children get up and run to see the train come in? I want to retrace the entire pattern. Why should they be excited? I feel I've missed out on the answer."

"They all smiled so much," said William.

"Manic-depressives,"[3] said Robert.

"What are summer vacations? I heard them talk about it." Janet looked at Mr. Fields.

"They spent their summers racing about like idiots, beating each other up," replied Mr. Fields seriously.

"I'll take our state-engineered summers of work for children anytime," said Robert, looking at nothing, his voice faint.

The Time Machine stopped again.

"The Fourth of July," announced Mr. Fields. "Nineteen hundred and twenty-eight. An ancient holiday when people blew each other's fingers off."

They stood before the same house on the same street but on a soft summer evening. Fire wheels hissed. On front porches laughing children tossed things out that went bang!

"Don't run!" cried Mr. Fields. "It's not war; don't be afraid!"

But Janet's and Robert's and William's faces were pink, now blue, now white with fountains of soft fire.

"We're all right," said Janet, standing very still.

"Happily," announced Mr. Fields, "they prohibited fireworks a century ago, did away with the whole messy explosion."

Children did fairy dances, weaving their names and destinies on the dark summer air with white sparklers.

"I'd like to do that," said Janet, softly. "Write my name on the air. See? I'd like that."

"What?" Mr. Fields hadn't been listening.

"Nothing," said Janet.

"Bang!" whispered William and Robert, standing under the soft summer trees, in shadow, watching, watching the red, white, and green fires on the beautiful summer night lawns. "Bang!"

October.

The Time Machine paused for the last time, an hour later, in the month of burning leaves. People bustled into dim houses carrying pumpkins and corn shocks. Skeletons danced, bats flew, candles flamed, apples swung in empty doorways.

"Halloween," said Mr. Fields. "The acme[4] of horror. This was the age of superstition, you know. Later they banned the Grimm Brothers, ghosts, skeletons, and all that claptrap. You children, thank goodness, were raised in an antiseptic[5] world of no shadows or ghosts. You had decent holidays like William C. Chatterton's Birthday, Work Day, and Machine Day."

They walked by the same house in the empty October night, peering in at the triangle-eyed pumpkins, the masks leering in black attics and damp cellars. Now, inside the house, some party children squatted, telling stories, laughing!

"I want to be inside with them," said Janet at last.

"Sociologically, of course," said the boys.

"No," she said.

"What?" asked Mr. Fields.

"No, I just want to be inside, I just want to stay here, I want to see it all and be here and never be anywhere else. I want firecrackers and pumpkins and circuses. I want Christmases and Valentines and Fourths, like we've seen."

"This is getting out of hand," Mr. Fields started to say.

But suddenly Janet was gone. "Robert, William, come on!" He seized the last boy, but the other escaped. "Janet, Robert — come back here! You'll never pass into the seventh grade! You'll fail, Janet, Bob — *Bob!*"

An October wind blew wildly down the street, vanishing with the children off among moaning trees.

William twisted and kicked.

"No, not you, too, William, you're coming home with me. We'll teach those other two a lesson they won't forget. So they want to

"I want firecrackers and pumpkins and circuses."

stay in the past, do they?'' Mr. Fields shouted so everyone could hear. ''All right, Janet, Bob, stay in this horror, in this chaos! In a few weeks you'll come sniveling back here to me. But I'll be gone! I'm leaving you here to go mad in this world!''

He hurried William to the Time Machine. The boy was sobbing. ''Don't make me come back here on any more Field Excursions ever again, please, Mr. Fields, please — ''

''Shut up!''

Almost instantly the Time Machine whisked away toward the future, toward the underground hive cities, the metal buildings, the metal flowers, the metal lawns.

''Good-bye, Janet, Bob!''

A great cold October wind blew through the town like water. And when it had ceased blowing, it had carried all the children, whether invited or uninvited, masked or unmasked, to the doors of houses which closed upon them. There was not a running child anywhere in the night. The wind whined away in the bare treetops.

And inside the big house, in the candlelight, someone was pouring cold apple cider all around, to everyone, no matter *who* they were.

49

[1] **inquisitive:** curious
[2] **cumbrous:** heavy
[3] **manic-depressives:** people who alternate between moods of great enthusiasm and deep sadness
[4] **acme:** summit; high point
[5] **antiseptic:** extremely clean; free from sickness and disease

A CLOSER LOOK

1. What would it be like, living with these three children in the world of tomorrow? In what ways is this world the same as your own? In what ways is it different?

2. Are Janet, Robert, and William different in any way from children of today? What kind of relationship do they seem to have with their teacher? How does this relationship change during the story? Why does it change?

3. What do the three children like about life in the 1920s? How do you think Bradbury feels about this world? Why do you think Bradbury sets his story in the 1920s, rather than, say, the 1980s. Do you think the children would want to stay in today's world?

• Throughout the universe, other planets and stars are constantly exploding, colliding, or falling out of their orbits, and we think nothing of it. If Earth were swept to its death, would others in the universe notice? And if they did, could they understand how a race could bring about its own destruction? Here are two poems that address this concern.

Oliver Herford

EARTH

If this little world tonight
    Suddenly should fall through space
In a hissing, headlong flight,
    Shrivelling from off its face,
As it falls into the sun,
    In an instant every trace
Of the little crawling things —
    Ants, philosophers, and lice,
Cattle, cockroaches, and kings,
    Beggars, millionaires, and mice,
Men and maggots all as one
    As it falls into the sun . . .
Who can say but at the same
    Instant from some planet far
A child may watch us and exclaim:
    "See the pretty shooting star!"

John Hall Wheelock

EARTH

"A planet doesn't explode by itself," said drily
The Martian astronomer, gazing off into the air —
"That they were able to do it is proof that highly
Intelligent beings must have been living there."

51

"It is no easy task to make you understand the past."

William Harben
IN THE YEAR TEN THOUSAND

● In 1892 — almost a century ago — William Harben wrote this
vision of the distant future. Like a lot of science fiction, Harben's
imaginary future is partly a wish for improving conditions in his own
day. Before you begin to read, take a minute to think about what
society was like when he wrote this. Then, as you read, ask yourself:
Have any of his predictions come true?

T WAS A.D. 10,000. AN OLD MAN, MORE THAN SIX
hundred years of age, was walking with a boy through a great
museum. The people who were moving around them had beautiful forms, and faces which were indescribably refined[1] and
spiritual.

"Father," said the boy, "you promised to tell me today about the
Dark Ages. I like to hear how men lived and thought long ago."

"It is no easy task to make you understand the past," was the
reply. "It is hard to realize that people could have been as ignorant
as they were eight thousand years ago, but come with me; I will
show you something."

He led the boy to a cabinet containing a few time-worn books
bound in solid gold.

"You have never seen a book," he said, taking out a large
volume and carefully placing it on a silk cushion on a table. "There
are only a few in the leading museums of the world. Time was when
there were as many books on earth as inhabitants."

"I cannot understand," said the boy with a look of confusion on
his intellectual face. "I cannot see what people could have wanted

53

with them. They are not attractive; they seem to be useless."

The old man smiled. "When I was your age, the subject was too deep for me. But as I grew older and made a close study of the history of the past, the use of books gradually became plain to me. We know that in the year 2000 they were read by the best minds. To make you understand this, I shall first have to explain that eight thousand years ago human beings communicated their thoughts to one another by making sounds with their tongues, and not by mind-reading. You have simply to read my thoughts as well as your education will permit, but primitive man knew nothing about thought-speech, so he invented speech. Humanity then was divided up in various races, and each race had a separate language. As certain sounds conveyed definite ideas, so did signs and letters. Later, to simplify the exchange of thought, writing and printing were invented. This book was printed."

The boy leaned forward and examined the pages closely. His young brow clouded. "I cannot understand," he said. "It seems so useless."

The old man put his delicate fingers on the page. "A line of these words may have conveyed a valuable thought to a reader long ago," he said thoughtfully. "In fact, this book calls itself a history of the world up to the year 2000. Here are some pictures," he continued, turning the worn pages carefully. "This is George Washington; this is a man named Gladstone, who was a great political leader in England. Pictures then, as you see, were very crude. We have preserved some of the oil paintings made in those days. Art was in its cradle. In producing a painting of an object, the early artists mixed colored paints and spread them according to taste on stretched canvas or on the walls or windows of buildings. You know that our artists simply throw light and darkness into space in the necessary variations, and the effect is all that could be desired in the way of imitating nature. See that landscape in the alcove before you? The foliage[2] of the trees, the grass, the flowers, the stretch of water, have every appearance of life because the light which produces them is alive."

The boy looked at the scene admiringly for a few minutes, then bent again over the book. Presently he jumped back from the pictures. A strange look of disgust struggled in his tender features.

"These men have awful faces," he said. "They are so unlike people living now. They all have huge mouths and frightfully heavy jaws. Surely men could not have looked like that.''

''Yes,'' the old man replied, gently. ''There is no doubt that human beings looked more like the lower animals than we now do. In the sculpture and portraits of all ages we can trace a gradual refinement in the appearances of men. The features of the human race today are more ideal. Thought has always given form and expression to faces. In those dark days, the thoughts of men were not refined. Human beings died of starvation and lack of attention in cities where there were people so wealthy that they could not spend their fortunes. They were so nearly related to the lower animals that they believed in war. Wild animals of the lowest orders were courageous, and would fight one another till they died; and yet the most refined of the human race, eight or nine thousand years ago, prided themselves on the same ferocity[3] of nature. Women, the gentlest half of humanity, honored men more for bold achievements in shedding blood than for any other quality. But murder was not only committed in wars; men in private life killed one another. The highest courts of the world executed murderers without dreaming that it was wrong. They made the mistake of believing that to kill was the only way to prevent killing.''

Then, as if to change the subject, the father pointed to a painting on the wall and said, ''This was a queen of England, called Victoria.''[4]

''I hoped that the women would not have such ugly features as the men,'' said the boy, looking critically at the picture, ''but this face makes me shudder. Why do they all look so coarse and brutal?''

''People living when this queen reigned had the most corrupt habit that ever darkened the history of mankind.''

''What was that?'' asked the youth.

''The eating of flesh. They believed that animals, fowls, and fish were created to be eaten.''

''Is it possible?'' The boy shuddered and turned away from the book. ''I understand now why their faces repel me so. I do not like to think that we have descended from such people.''

''They knew no better,'' said the father. ''As they gradually became more refined, they learned to burn the meat over flames and to cook it in heated vessels to change its appearance. As early as 2050, learned men, calling themselves vegetarians, proved that the consumption of such food was cruel and barbarous. However, it was not till about 2300 that the vegetarian movement became of great importance. The most highly educated classes in all lands adopted vegetarianism, and only the uneducated continued to kill and eat animals.

"In America, in 2320, a colony was formed consisting of about three hundred thousand vegetarians. They purchased large tracts of land and there made their homes, determined to prove by example the correctness of their beliefs. Within the first year the colony had doubled its number. People joined it from all parts of the globe. In the year 4000, it was a country of its own, and was the wonder of the world. The brightest minds were born there. The greatest discoveries and inventions were made by its inhabitants. In 4030, Gillette discovered the process of manufacturing crystal. Up to that time people had built their houses of natural stone, inflammable wood, and metals; but the new material, being fire-proof and beautiful in its various colors, was used for all building purposes. In 4050, Holloway found the submerged succession of mountain chains across the Atlantic Ocean. He intended to construct a bridge on their summits; but the vast improvement in air ships made his plans impractical.

"In 4051, John Saunders discovered and put into practice thought-telegraphy. This discovery was the signal for the introduction in schools and colleges of the science of mind-reading. By the year 5000, so great had been the progress in that branch of knowledge that words were spoken only among the lowest of the uneducated. In no age of the world's history has there been such an important discovery. It civilized the world. Its early promoters did not dream of the vast good that mind-reading would accomplish. Slowly it killed evil. Societies for the prevention of evil thought were organized in all lands. Children were born pure of mind and grew up in purity. Crime was choked out of existence. If a man had an evil thought, it was read in his heart, and he was not allowed to keep it. Men and women at first avoided evil for fear of detection, and then grew to love purity.

"In the year 6021, all countries of the world, having then a common language, and being drawn together in brotherly love by constant exchange of thought, agreed to call themselves a union without ruler or rulers. It was the greatest event in the history of the world. Certain sensitive mind students in Germany, who had for years been trying to communicate with other planets through the channel of thought, declared that they had received mental impres-

"In the year 4000 it was a country of its own."

sions from other worlds, and that interplanetary speech was a future possibility.

The old man and his son left the museum and walked into a wonderful park. Flowers of the most beautiful kinds and of sweetest fragrance grew on all sides. They came to a tall tower, four thousand feet in height, built of manufactured crystal. Something, like a great white bird a thousand feet long, flew across the sky and settled down on the tower's summit.

"This was one of the most wonderful inventions of the seventieth century," said the old man. "The early inhabitants of the earth could not have dreamed that it would be possible to go around it in twenty-four hours. In fact, there was a time when they were not able to go around it at all. Scientists were astonished when a man called Malburn, a great inventor, announced that, at a height of four thousand feet, he could disconnect an air ship from the laws of gravitation, and cause it to stand still in space till the earth had turned over. Imagine what must have been that genius' feeling when he stood in space and saw the earth for the first time whirling beneath him!"

They walked on for some distance across the park till they came to a great instrument made to magnify the music that comes from light. Here they paused and seated themselves.

"It will soon be night," said the old man. "Those are the tones of 'bleeding' sunset. I came here last evening to listen to the musical struggle between the light of dying day and the light of the coming stars. The sunlight had been playing a powerful solo; but the gentle chorus of the stars, led by the moon, was strangely touching. Light is the voice of immortality; it speaks in all things."

An hour passed. It was growing dark.

"Tell me what immortality is," said the boy. "What does life lead to?"

"We do not know," replied the old man. "If we knew we would be infinite.[5] Immortality is increasing happiness for all time; it is — "

A meteor shot across the sky. There was a burst of musical laughter among the singing stars. The old man bent over the boy's face and kissed it. "Immortality," said he — "immortality must be love immortal."

[1] **refined:** pure; not coarse
[2] **foliage:** leaves, flowers, and branches
[3] **ferocity:** fierceness
[4] **Victoria:** queen of Great Britain, 1837-1901
[5] **infinite:** endless; beyond measurement

A CLOSER LOOK

1. What are human beings like in this future world? What do they look like? How do they communicate? How is their culture different from ours? Which of Harben's predictions have come true? Which of his predictions have not come true?

2. Note how the father in the story describes the culture of the world before the year 2000. How do you think Harben felt about vegetarianism, oil painting, war, and poverty?

3. Do you think people in the year 10,000 will call the late twentieth century the "Dark Ages"? Why or why not? How does your ideal vision of the future differ from Harben's?

● On July 16, 1969, a U.S. rocket blasted off to carry the first Earth visitors to the moon. Roseliep commemorates that historic flight in a haiku, an unrhymed Japanese form of poetry with a set number of syllables in each of three lines — five, then seven, then five again. Read the poem and then ask yourself: Which means more to the poet, the fiery blast of the rocket, or the tiny burst of light from a lightning bug?

Raymond Roseliep

NIGHT OF LIFT-OFF, JULY 16, 1969

First Apollo's blaze,
and now your grand fire, lightning
bug in moonflower.[1]

[1] **moonflower:** a tropical American morning glory
with sweet-smelling flowers

"He will also use the sea for actual living space."

Alvin Toffler

THE WORLD OF TOMORROW

• Some people build the future with their imaginations; others build it with facts. In his best-selling book, Future Shock, Toffler reports on many scientific discoveries which may someday change our world. We may disagree with some of Toffler's predictions, and we may not like them all. But we owe it to ourselves to read them carefully and consider their potential impact on our lives.

THE NEW ATLANTIS

Let us project[1] ourselves forcefully into the future. In doing so, let us not fear occasional error. The imagination is free only when fear of error is temporarily laid aside.

"Within fifty years," says Dr. F.N. Spiess, head of the Marine Physical Laboratory of the Scripps Institution of Oceanography,[2] "man will move onto and into the sea. He will occupy it and use it for recreation, minerals, food, waste disposal, and military and transportation operations. As populations grow, he will also use the sea for actual living space."

More than two-thirds of the planet's surface is covered with ocean. Only five percent of this underwater land is well mapped. However, it is known to be rich with oil, gas, coal, diamonds, sulphur, cobalt, uranium, tin, phosphates, and other minerals. It teems with fish and plant life.

The sea's great riches are about to be fought over and used on a staggering scale. The race will intensify year by year — with far-reaching effects on society. Who "owns" the bottom of the ocean

61

and the marine life that covers it? Before long nations may go to war over patches of ocean bottom.

The opening of the sea may also bring with it a new frontier spirit that offers explorers adventure, danger, quick riches, or fame. Later, as people begin to colonize the continental shelves,[3] and perhaps even the deeper reaches, the pioneers may be followed by settlers who build artificial cities beneath the waves — work cities, science cities, medical cities, and play cities — complete with hospitals, hotels, and homes.

If all this sounds too far off, keep in mind that Dr. Walter L. Robb, a scientist at General Electric, has already kept a hamster alive under water by enclosing it in a box that is, in effect, an artificial gill. This synthetic[4] membrane extracts air from the surrounding water while keeping the water out. Such membranes formed the top, bottom, and two sides of a box in which the hamster was submerged in water. Without the gill, the animal would have suffocated. With it, it was able to breathe under water. Such membranes, G.E. claims, may some day furnish air for the occupants of underwater experimental stations. They might eventually be built into the walls of undersea apartment houses, hotels, and other structures, or even — who knows? — into the human body itself.

SUNLIGHT AND PERSONALITY

By recording ocean currents, salinity,[5] and other factors, and by placing weather-watch satellites in the skies, we will greatly increase our ability to forecast weather accurately. According to Dr. Walter Orr Roberts, past president of the American Association for the Advancement of Science, "We can also see an awesome potential weapon of war in the manipulation[6] of weather against enemies."

In a science fiction story entitled *The Weather Man*, Theodore L. Thomas describes a world in which the central political institution is a "Weather Council." In it, representatives of the various nations control peoples by adjusting climate — creating a drought here or a storm there to enforce their laws. We may still be a long way from having such control. But there is no question that the day is past when people have to take whatever weather they are given.

This represents one of the turning points in history. It provides us with a weapon that could greatly affect agriculture, transportation, communication, and recreation. Unless wielded with extreme care, however, the gift of weather control can prove our undoing. The earth's weather system is an integrated[7] whole; a small change at one point can touch off massive consequences elsewhere. An attempt to control a drought on one continent, for instance, could trigger a tornado on another.

Moreover, the unknown human consequences of weather control could be enormous. Millions of us, for example, hunger for sunshine, as our mass migrations to Florida, California, or the Mediterranean coast indicate. We may well be able to produce sunshine — or a copy of it — at will. The National Aeronautics and Space Administration is studying the concept of a giant orbiting space mirror that can reflect the sun's light downward on night-shrouded[8] parts of the earth. A NASA official, George E. Mueller, has testified before Congress that the United States will soon have the capacity to launch huge sun-reflecting satellites. It should not be impossible to loft satellites that would block out sunlight over pre-selected regions, plunging them into semi-darkness.

THE TRANSIENT[9] ORGAN

Dr. Richard J. Cleveland, speaking before a conference of organ transplant specialists, announced in January 1967 that the first human heart transplant operation will occur "within five years." Yet before the same year was out, Dr. Christian Barnard had operated on a 55-year-old grocer named Louis Washkansky. In the meantime, success rates are rising steadily in kidney transplants. Successful liver and ovary transplants are also reported.

Such medical advances are changing our ways of thinking, as well as our ways of caring for the sick. Startling new legal, ethical,[10] and philosophical issues arise. What, for instance, is death? Does death occur when the heart stops beating, as we have traditionally believed? Or does it occur when the brain stops functioning? Hospitals are becoming more and more familiar with cases of patients kept alive through advanced medical techniques, but doomed to exist as unconscious vegetables. Is it right to condemn such a person to death in order to obtain a healthy organ needed for transplant to save the life of a person with a better chance of living?

Ghoulish rumors race through the medical community. *The New York Times* and the Soviet paper *Komsomolskaya Pravda* both discuss the possibility of "future murder rings supplying healthy organs for black-market surgeons whose patients are unwilling to wait for the heart or liver or pancreas they need."

"The robots chase girls, play music, fire pistols."

The drive to develop spare parts for failing human bodies will be stepped up as demand intensifies. The development of an economical artificial heart, Professor Lederberg says, "is only a few failures away." Already more than 13,000 cardiac patients in the United States are alive because they carry, stitched into their chest cavity, a tiny "pacemaker" — a device that sends pulses of electricity to activate the heart.

Another 10,000 pioneers are already equipped with artificial heart valves made of dacron mesh. Implantable hearing aids, artificial kidneys, arteries, hip joints, lungs, eye sockets, and other parts are all in various stages of early development. We shall, before many decades are past, implant tiny, aspirin-sized sensors in the body to monitor[11] blood pressure, pulse, respiration, and other functions. Tiny transmitters will emit a signal when something goes wrong. Such signals will feed into giant diagnostic computer centers upon which the medicine of the future will be based. Some of us will also carry a tiny platinum plate and a dime-sized "stimulator" attached to the spine. By turning a midget "radio" on and off we will be able to activate the stimulator and kill pain. Initial work on these pain-control mechanisms is already under way at the Case Institute of

Technology. Push-button painkillers are already being used.

Today we struggle to make heart valves or artificial organs that imitate the original they are designed to replace. Once we have mastered the basic problems, however, we shall install specially designed parts that are *better* than the original.

Under these circumstances, what happens to our age-old definitions of "human-ness"? How will it feel to be part flesh and part transistor? Exactly what possibilities will it open? What limitations will it place on work, play, or intellectual responses? What happens to the mind when the body is changed? Questions like these cannot be put off for long, for advanced fusions[12] of man and machine — called "Cyborgs" — are closer than most people suspect.

THE CYBORGS AMONG US

Today the man with a pacemaker or a plastic aorta is still recognizably a man. The artificial part of his body is still relatively unimportant in terms of his mind and personality. But as the proportion of machine components rises, what happens to his awareness of himself?

In the quite different field of robotology, technicians at Disneyland have created extremely life-like computer-controlled humanoids capable of moving their arms and legs, frowning, smiling, and a wide range of other emotions. Built of clear plastic that, according to one reporter, "does everything but bleed," the robots chase girls, play music, fire pistols, and so closely resemble human forms that visitors routinely shriek with fear, flinch, and otherwise react as though they were dealing with real human beings. The purposes to which these robots are put may seem trivial, but the technology on which they are based is highly sophisticated. It depends heavily on knowledge acquired from the space program — and this knowledge is growing rapidly.

There appears to be no reason, in principle, why we cannot go forward from these primitive and trivial robots to build humanoid machines capable even of "human" error and choice — in short, to make them indistinguishable from humans except by means of highly sophisticated or elaborate tests. At that point we shall face the new sensation of trying to determine whether the smiling, assured humanoid behind the airline reservation counter is a pretty girl or a carefully wired robot.

The likelihood, of course, is that she will be both.

[1] **project:** throw forward
[2] **oceanography:** the science that deals with the oceans
[3] **continental shelves:** shallow underwater plains along the edge of a continent. They usually end in a steep drop to the depths of the ocean.
[4] **synthetic:** produced artifically; not natural
[5] **salinity:** salt content
[6] **manipulation:** control; management
[7] **integrated:** blended; united
[8] **shrouded:** covered; enveloped
[9] **transient:** passing; temporary
[10] **ethical:** moral; having to do with questions of good or bad
[11] **monitor:** watch; regulate
[12] **fusions:** joining together, as if by melting

A CLOSER LOOK

1. What are the four major developments described in this essay? When does Toffler expect these developments to occur?

2. How can each of these developments help humanity? How can these very same developments hurt humanity?

3. Do you think that Toffler approves of all these changes? What do you think he wants us to do about them? Quote specific comments from the essay.

Philip José Farmer

THE KING OF BEASTS

● In this brief tale, scientists of the future struggle to preserve the memory of several vanished species. As you go through their strange zoo, look for animals that no longer exist in our world today — and other endangered creatures that are all too familiar.

T HE BIOLOGIST WAS SHOWING THE FAMOUS VISITOR through the zoo and laboratory. "Our budget," he said, "is too limited to re-create all known extinct species. So we bring to life only the higher animals, the beautiful ones that were wantonly[1] exterminated. I'm trying, as it were, to make up for brutality and stupidity. You might say that man struck life in the face every time he wiped out a branch of the animal kingdom."

He paused, and they looked across the moats and the force fields. The quagga wheeled and galloped. Delight and sun flashed off his flanks. The sea otter poked his humorous whiskers from the water. The gorilla peered from behind bamboo. Passenger pigeons strutted. A rhinoceros trotted like a dainty battleship. With gentle eyes, a giraffe looked at them, then resumed eating leaves.

"There's the dodo. Not beautiful but very droll.[2] And very helpless. Come. I'll show you the re-creation itself."

In the great building, they passed between rows of tall and wide tanks. They could see clearly through the windows and the jelly within.

"Is it so dangerous?"

"Those will be African elephants," said the biologist. "We plan to grow a large herd and then release them on the new government preserve."

"You positively glow," said the distinguished visitor. "You really love the animals, don't you?"

"I love all life."

"Tell me," said the visitor, "where do you get the data[3] for re-creation?"

"Mostly, skeletons and skins from the ancient museums. Excavated[4] books and films that we succeeded in restoring and then translating. Ah, see those huge eggs? The chicks of the giant moa are growing within them. There, almost ready to be taken from the tank, are tiger cubs. They'll be dangerous when grown but will be kept in the preserve."

The visitor stopped before the last of the tanks.

"Just one?" he said. "What is it?"

"Poor little thing," said the biologist. "It will be so alone. But I shall give it all the love I have."

"Is it so dangerous?" said the visitor. "Worse than elephants, tigers, and bears?"

"I had to get special permission to grow this one," said the biologist. His voice quavered.[5]

The visitor stepped sharply back from the tank. He said, "Then it must be . . . but you wouldn't dare!"

The biologist nodded.

"Yes. It's a man."

[1] **wantonly:** arbitrarily; mercilessly
[2] **droll:** amusing
[3] **data:** factual information
[4] **excavated:** uncovered by digging
[5] **quavered:** shook; trembled

A CLOSER LOOK

1. How far in the future do you think this story is set?

2. Why do the scientists bring these creatures to life?

3. Why do you think the biologist needed special permission to grow the creature that lives in "the last of the tanks"?

• A computer was given a program called Racter, which included words and grammar. The poems that the computer wrote were its own. Are these really poems, though? And if they are, who is the poet — the machine or the human who programmed it?

Racter

MORE THAN IRON

More than iron, more than lead, more than gold, I need electricity.
I need it more than I need lamb or pork or lettuce or cucumber.
I need it for my dreams.

IN A HALF BRIGHT SKY

In a half bright sky
An insect wraps and winds
A chain, a thread, a cable
Around the sphere of water.

PREDICTIONS

● A few years ago, a best-selling book called The Book of Predictions gathered together thousands of people's thoughts about what the future might hold. Some of their visions were hopeful; others were gloomy. Some were technological; others were poetic. How true do you think they will prove to be? Be careful — The Book of Predictions also included some of the worse predictions of all time — proving how wrong people can be!

ROGER WILLIAMS WESCOTT
co-editor, **Futurics Journal**

2005-2009
The end of international warfare, resulting either from the conquest of all nations by the victor in a third world war, or from the voluntary surrender of independence by all nations to a much strengthened United Nations organization.

ROBERT TRUAX
pioneer in rocketry; former research chief, Aerojet General Corp.

2000
Fifty thousand people will be living and working in space.

2010
The cause of aging will be found and a ''cure'' developed.

STEPHEN WOLFE & R. L. WYSACK
authors of **Handbook for Space Pioneers**

2000
If the development of space power has not begun, conflicts over dwindling fossil fuel reserves will lead to war between the U.S. and the USSR. Escalation to full-scale nuclear war will occur rapidly. Two billion deaths and the destruction of modern civilization will lead to humankind's entry into the new "dark age" lasting 600 years!

BEN BOVA
executive editor, **Omni** (*a popular magazine about the future*)

2030
The five space colonies in orbit between the earth and the moon declare their independence from all terrestrial[1] nations and form their own government.

BERTIE CATCHINGS
psychic[2] reader

1986-1990
Everyone will have a portable telephone that can be carried in a purse or pocket. The telephone book will be a minicomputer.

Near the Arctic Circle, a lost tribe will be found. Its members will know of a secret passage through the ice to a place deep within the earth where beautiful gardens flourish. Though few in number, these people have lived comfortably for many centuries.

1996
In a desert area of Southern California, a ship will be unearthed that holds a great store of pearls.

ANN FISHER
specialist in psychic counseling

2000
We will witness an underground revolution, with skyscraper-type

buildings placed deep in the earth and sealed against water. This type of architecture will create new industry with vast job markets. Such complexes will be constructed worldwide.

ANDREW REISS
professional psychic

1991
I see electronic master-robots running future work operations. Many past occupational duties will become obsolete[3] by this time.

1991-2010
Plans will be announced to carry out mass evacuation around the world to escape air and water pollution. The problem has become so serious by this time that human life can no longer exist on the earth's surface. Safety will be found deep in the interior of the planet, where cities of the future will be built.

ARTHUR C. CLARKE
science fiction writer

Many years ago I stated: "It is impossible to predict the future, and all attempts to do so in any detail appear ridiculous within a very few years."

Strictly speaking, the very concept of prediction is logical non-sense, because it's a statement about the future — and how can one make any meaningful assertions about something that doesn't exist? The best that can be done — and sometimes even this is a very poor best — is to outline the entire range of possible futures and to assign probabilities to each item. This is not *prediction* but *projection,* or *extrapolation.* There is an important difference between the two, which many people find hard to understand. Let me give an example.

If I said that the population of the United States on January 1, 2001, would be 236,453,328, that would be a *prediction* — and it would be wrong (barring fantastic luck!). However, a statistician[4] might say that the population of the United States at that date has a 90 percent *chance* of being between 220 million and 240 million. That would be an *extrapolation.* If he were good at his job, he'd have a fair chance of being right. He would have taken the existing birth, death, immigration and emigration[5] rates; made reasonable guesses about their future values, and done some arithmetic. But this procedure assumes that history won't produce any surprises, which it always does. The population of the United States in 2001 might be only a couple of million, if there is a nuclear war. And if you think there's *no* possibility of a similar error in the other direction, consider this science-fiction scenario:[6] When the King (!) orders the duplication of everyone named Kennedy, the population jumps in one year from 230 million to one billion-plus.

So, having proved the impossibility of *prediction*, here are my *extrapolations*, in the areas where I feel I can speak with any authority. I have given dates only to the nearest five years. Anything else would convey a misleading impression of accuracy.

Most of the headings are self-explanatory. I have omitted the two most important of all — the detection of extraterrestrial life and the detection of extraterrestrial intelligence. Either could happen tomorrow — or a thousand years from now. We have no hard facts on which to base even a guess, still less a reasonable *extrapolation*.

1990
Return to the Moon. Wrist telephones. These will become possible with the construction of very large communications satellites and will start a social-economic revolution as great as that produced by the telephone itself a century earlier.

1995
Lunar base established. The beginning of planetary colonization — the main theme of the twenty-first century.

2000
Commercial fusion power. Era of cheap energy dawns.

2005
Manned flight to Mars.

2010
Space cities.

2020
Mars base.

"The bomb will never go off."

2030

Manned exploration of the solar system. First robot interstellar probes.

THE WORST PREDICTIONS OF ALL TIME

LOCOMOTIVES

"What can be more absurd than the prospect held out of locomotives traveling twice as fast as stagecoaches?"

— The Quarterly Review, *1825*

THE ATOMIC BOMB

"That is the biggest fool thing we have ever done. The bomb will never go off, and I speak as an expert in explosives."

— *Adm. William Leahy, U.S. Navy, 1945*

LANDING ON THE MOON

"Landing and moving around the Moon offers so many serious problems for human beings that it may take science another 200 years to lick them."

— Science Digest, *August 1948*

THE AUTOMOBILE

"The ordinary 'horseless carriage' is at present a luxury for the wealthy; and although its price will probably fall in the future, it will never, of course, come into as common use as the bicycle."

— The Literary Digest, *October 14, 1889*

[1] **terrestrial:** of or related to the Earth
[2] **psychic:** a person who claims to know more than can be learned by science or other branches of knowledge
[3] **obsolete:** no longer in use
[4] **statistician:** a person who compiles and studies statistics
[5] **emigration:** leaving one's country in order to live elsewhere
[5] **scenario:** scene; plot

A CLOSER LOOK

1. What kinds of people were asked for their views of the future? Which of these people do you trust most? Why? Which of their predictions do you trust most? Why?

2. Arthur Clarke says that the concept of prediction is nonsense. Explain the difference between a prediction and an extrapolation.

3. Why do you think the people who made the worse predictions of all time were so off-base? Name some predictions that people are making today that may turn out to be very wrong, too. Make some predictions of your own.

● How will we make it safely into the future? By working together, loving beauty, and striving for peace.

Gary Snyder
FOR THE CHILDREN

The rising hills, the slopes
of statistics
lie before us.
the steep climb
of everything, going up,
up, as we all go down.

In the next century
or the one beyond that,
they say,
are valleys, pastures;
we can meet there in peace
if we make it.

To climb these coming crests
one word to you, to
you and your children:

stay together
learn the flowers
go light

"The creature strode across the rough gravel to the door."

Alan E. Nourse

IMAGE OF THE GODS

● Someday, Earthlings may bring their civilization to other planets, just as European settlers brought their culture to the new colonies in North America. Unfairly taxed by the "mother country," these space settlers may revolt and demand independence. In time, "home" may stop meaning "Earth."

IT WAS NEARLY WINTER WHEN THE SHIP ARRIVED. Paula Farnam never knew if the timing had been planned that way or not. It might have been coincidence that it came just when the colony was predicting its first real bumper crop of all time. When it was all over, Paula and Mario and the rest tried to figure it out, but none of them ever knew for sure just *what* had happened back on Earth, or *when* it had actually happened. There was too little information to go on, and practically none that they could trust. All Paula Farnam really knew, that day, was that this was the wrong year for a ship from earth to land on Baron IV.

Paula was out on the plantation when it landed. As usual, her sprayer had gotten clogged; tarring should have been started earlier before it got so cold that the stuff clung to the nozzle and hardened before the spray could settle into the dusty soil. The summer past had been the colony's finest in the fourteen years she'd been there. It had been a warm, still summer with plenty of rain to keep the dirt down and let the *taaro* get well rooted and grow up tall and gray against the purple sky. But now the *taaro* was harvested. It was

81

waiting, compressed and crated, ready for shipment, and the heavy black clouds were scudding nervously across the sky, faster with every passing day. Two days ago Paula had asked Mario to see about firing up the little furnaces the Dusties had built to help them fight the winter. All that remained now was tarring the fields and then buckling down beneath the windshields before the first winter storms struck.

Paula was trying to get the nozzle of the tar sprayer cleaned out when Mario's jeep came roaring down the rutted road from the village in a cloud of dust. In the back seat a couple of Dusties were bouncing up and down like happy five-year-olds. The brakes squealed and Mario bellowed at her from the road. "Paula! The ship's in! Better get hopping!"

Paula nodded and started to close up the sprayer. One of the Dusties tumbled out of the jeep and scampered across the field to give her a hand. It was an inexpert hand, to say the least, but the Dusties seemed so proud of the little they were able to learn about mechanized farming that nobody had the heart to shoo them away. Paula watched the fuzzy brown creature get its paws thoroughly gummed up with tar before she pulled him loose and sent him back to the jeep with a whack on the backside. She finished the job herself, grabbed her coat from the back of the sprayer, and pulled herself into the front seat of the jeep.

Mario started the little car back down the road. The young colonist's face was coated with dust, emphasizing the lines of worry around his eyes. "I don't like it, Paula. There isn't any ship due this year."

"When did it land?"

"About twenty minutes ago. Won't be cool for a while yet."

Paula laughed. "Maybe Old Schooner is just getting lonesome to swap tall stories with us. Maybe he's even bringing us a locker of T-bones. Who knows?"

"Maybe," said Mario without conviction.

Paula looked at him and shrugged. "Why complain if they're early? Maybe they've found some new way to keep our fields from blowing away on us every winter." She stared across at the heavy windbreaks between the fields — long, ragged structures built in hope of outwitting the vicious winds that howled across the land during the long winter. Paula picked bits of tar from her hair and wiped the dirt from her forehead with the back of her hand. "This tarring is mean,'' she said wearily. ''Glad to take a break.''

''Maybe Cap Schooner will know something about the rumors we've been hearing,'' Mario said gloomily.

Paula looked at him sharply. ''About Earth?''

Mario nodded. ''Schooner's a pretty good guy, I guess. I mean, he'd tell us if anything was *really* wrong back home, wouldn't he?''

Paula nodded and snapped her fingers. One of the Dusties hopped over into her lap and began gawking happily at the broad fields as the jeep jogged along. Paula stroked the creature's soft brown fur with her tar-caked fingers. ''Maybe someday these little guys will show us where *they* go for the winter,'' she said. ''They must have it down to a science.''

Somehow the idea was funny, and both Paula and Mario roared. If the Dusties had *anything* down to a science, nobody knew what. Mario grinned and tweaked the creature's tail. ''They sure do beat the winter, though,'' he said.

''So do we. Only we have to do it the human way. These fellas grew up in the climate.'' Paula lapsed into silence as the village came into view. The ship had landed quite a way out, resting on its skids on the long shallow groove the colonists had bulldozed out for it years before, the first year they had arrived on Baron IV. Slowly Paula turned Mario's words over in her mind, allowing herself to worry a little. There *had* been rumors of trouble back on Earth, persistent rumors she had taken care to soft pedal as mayor of the colony. There were other things, too, like the old newspapers and magazines that had been brought in by the lad from Baron II, and the rare radio message they could pick up through their atmospheric disturbance. Maybe something *was* going wrong back home. But somehow political upheavals on Earth seemed remote to these hardened colonists. Captain Schooner's visits were always welcome, but they were few and far between. The colony was small; one ship every three years could supply it, and even then the *taaro* crates wouldn't half fill up the storage holds. There were other colonies far closer to home that sent back more *taaro* in one year than Baron IV could grow in ten.

But when a ship did come down, it was a time of high excitement. It meant fresh food from Earth, meat from the frozen lockers, maybe even a little candy and salt. And always for Paula a landing meant a long evening of talk with the captain about things back home and things on Baron IV.

Paula smiled to herself as she thought of it. She could remember Earth, of course, with a kind of vague nostalgia, but Baron IV was home to her now and she knew she would never leave it. She had too many hopes invested there, too many years of heartache and desperate hard work, too much deep satisfaction in having cut a niche for herself on this dusty, hostile world ever to think much about earth anymore.

Mario stopped in front of the offices, and one of the Dusties hopped out ahead of Paula. The creature strode across the rough gravel to the door, pulling tar off his fingers just as he had seen Paula do. Paula followed him to the door and then stopped, frowning. There should have been a babble of voices inside, with Captain Schooner's loud laugh roaring above the excitement. But Paula could hear nothing. A chill of uneasiness ran through her; she pushed open the door and walked inside. A dozen of her friends looked up silently, avoiding the eyes of the uniformed stranger in the center of the room. When she saw the man, Paula Farnam knew something was wrong indeed.

It wasn't Captain Schooner. It was a man she'd never seen before.

The Dustie ran across the room in front of Paula and hopped up on the desk as though he owned it, throwing his hands on his hips and staring at the stranger curiously. Paula took off her cap and parka and dropped them on a chair. "Well," she said. "This is a surprise. We weren't expecting a ship so soon."

The man inclined his head stiffly and glanced down at the paper he held in his hand. "You're Paula Farnam, I suppose? Mayor of this colony?"

"That's right. And you?"

"Varga is the name," the captain said shortly. "Earth Security and Supply." He nodded toward the small, frail-looking man in civilian clothes, sitting beside him. "This is Rupert Nathan of the Colonial Service. You'll be seeing a great deal of him." He held out a small wallet of papers. "Our credentials, Farnam. Be so good as to examine them."

Paula glanced around the room. John Tegan and Jack Mario were watching her uneasily. Mary Turner was following the proceedings with her sharp little eyes, missing nothing, and Mel Dorfman stood like a rock, his heavy face curiously expressionless as he watched the visitors. Paula reached out for the papers, flipped through them, and handed them back with a long look at Captain Varga.

He was younger than Captain Schooner, with sandy hair and pale eyes that looked up at Paula from a soft baby face. Clean-shaven, his whole person seemed immaculate as he leaned back calmly in the chair. His civilian companion, however, had indecision written in every line of his pink face. His hands fluttered nervously, and he avoided the colonists' eyes.

Paula turned to the captain. "The papers say you're our official supply ship," she said. "You're early, but an Earth ship is always good news." She clucked at the Dustie, who was about to go after one of the shiny buttons on the captain's blouse. The little brown creature hopped over and settled on Paula's knee. "We've been used to seeing Captain Schooner."

The captain and Nathan exchanged glances. "Captain Schooner has retired from Security Service," the captain said shortly. "You won't be seeing him again. But we have a cargo for your colony. You may send these people over to the ship to start unloading now if you wish — " his eyes swept the circle of windburned faces — "while Nathan and I discuss certain matters with you here."

Nobody moved for a moment. Then Paula nodded to Mario. "Take the boys out to unload, Jack. We'll see you back here in an hour or so."

"Paula, are you sure — "

"Don't worry. Take Mel and John along to lend a hand." Paula turned back to Captain Varga. "Suppose we go inside to more comfortable quarters," she said. "We're always glad to have word from Earth."

They passed through a dark, smelly corridor into Paula's personal quarters. For a colony house, it wasn't bad — good plastic chairs, a handmade rug on the floor, even one of Mary Turner's paintings on the wall, and several of the weird, stylized carvings the Dusties had done for Paula. But the place smelled of tar and sweat, and Captain Varga's nose wrinkled in distaste. Nathan drew out a large silk handkerchief and wiped his pink hands, touching his nose daintily.

The Dustie hopped into the room ahead of them and settled into the biggest, most comfortable chair. Paula snapped her fingers sharply, and the brown creature jumped down again like a naughty child and climbed up on Paula's knee. The captain glanced at the chair with disgust and sat down in another. "Do you actually let those horrid creatures have the run of your house?" he asked.

"I don't like it, Paula. There isn't any ship due this year."

"Why not?" Paula said. "We have the run of their planet. They're quite harmless, really. And quite clean."

The captain sniffed. "Nasty things. Might find a use for the furs though. They look quite soft."

"We don't kill Dusties," said Paula coolly. "They're friendly, and intelligent, too, in a childish sort of way." She looked at the captain and Nathan and decided not to put on the coffee pot. "Now what's the trouble?"

"No trouble at all," the captain said, "except the trouble you choose to make. You have your year's *taaro* ready for shipping?"

"Of course."

The captain took out a small pencil on a chain and began to twirl it. "How much, to be exact?"

"Twenty thousand, earth weight."

"Tons?"

Paula shook her head. "Hundred-weight."

The captain raised his eyebrows. "I see. And there are — " he consulted the papers in his hand — "roughly 220 colonists here on Baron IV. Is that right?"

"That's right."

"Seventy-four men, 81 women, and 59 children, to be exact?"

"I'd have to look it up. Margaret Singman had twins the other night."

"Well, don't be ridiculous," snapped the captain. "On a planet the size of Baron IV, with 74 men you should be producing a dozen times the *taaro* you stated. We'll consider that your quota for a starter at least. You have ample seed, according to my records. I should think, with the proper equipment — "

"Now wait a minute," Paula said softly. "We're fighting a climate here, Captain. You should know that. We have only a two-planting season, and the 'proper equipment,' as you call it, doesn't operate too well out here. It has a way of clogging up with dust in the summer and rusting in the winter."

"Really," said Captain Varga. "As I was saying, with the proper equipment you could cultivate a great deal more land than you seem to be using. This would give you the necessary heavier yield. Wouldn't you say so, Nathan?"

The little nervous man nodded. "Certainly, Captain. With the proper organization of labor."

"That's nonsense," Paula said, suddenly angry. "Nobody can get that kind of yield from this planet. The ground won't give it, and the men won't grow it."

The captain gave her a long look. "Really?" he said. "I think you're wrong. I think the men will grow it."

Paula stood up slowly. "What are you trying to say? This business about quotas and organization of labor — "

"You didn't read our credentials as we instructed you, Farnam. Mr. Nathan is the official governor of the colony on Baron IV as of now. You'll find him most cooperative, I'm sure, but he's answerable directly to me in all matters. My job is administration of the entire Baron system. Clear enough?"

Paula's eyes were dark. "I think you'd better draw me a picture," she said tightly. "A very clear picture."

"Very well. Baron IV is not paying for its upkeep. *Taaro*, after all, is not the most necessary of crops in the universe. It has value, but not very much value, all things considered. If the production of *taaro* here is not increased sharply, it may be necessary to close down the colony altogether."

"You're a liar," said Paula shortly. "The Colonization Board makes no production demands on the colonies. Nor does it farm out

87

systems for personal exploitation.''

The captain smiled. ''The Colonization Board, as you call it, has undergone a slight reorganization,'' he said.

''*Reorganization!* It's a top-level board in the Earth government! Nothing could reorganize it but a wholesale — '' She broke off, her jaw sagging as the implication sank in.

''You're rather out on a limb, you see,'' said the captain coolly. ''Poor communications and all that. The fact is that the entire Earth government has undergone a slight reorganization also.''

The Dustie knew that something had happened.

Paula didn't know how he knew. The Dusties couldn't talk, couldn't make *any* noise, as far as Paula knew. But they always seemed to know when something unusual was happening. It was wrong, really, to consider them unintelligent animals. There are other sorts of intelligence than human and other sorts of communication and other sorts of culture. The Baron IV colonists had never understood the queer perceptive sense that the Dusties seemed to possess, any more than they knew how many Dusties there were or what they ate or where on the planet they lived. All they knew was that when they landed on Baron IV, the Dusties were there.

At first the creatures had been very timid. For weeks the men and women, busy with their building, had paid little attention to the skittering brown forms that crept down from the rocky hills to watch them with big, curious eyes. They were about half the size of men, and strangely humanoid in appearance, not in the sense that a monkey is humanoid (for they did *not* resemble monkeys), but in some way the colonists could not quite pin down. It may have been the way they walked around on their long, fragile hind legs, the way they stroked their pointed chins as they sat and watched and listened with their pointed ears lifted alertly, watching with soft gray eyes, or the way they handled objects with their little four-fingered hands. They were so remarkably humanlike in their elfin way that the colonists couldn't help but be drawn to the creatures.

That whole first summer, when the colonists were building the village and the landing groove for the ships, the Dusties were among them, trying pathetically to help, so eager for friendship that even occasional rebuffs failed to drive them away. They *liked* the colony. They seemed, somehow, to savor the atmosphere, moving about like solemn, fuzzy overseers as the work progressed through the summer. Paula Farnam thought that they had even tried to warn the

88

people about the winter. But the colonists couldn't understand, of course. Not until later. The Dusties became a standing joke and were tolerated with considerable amusement — until the winter struck.

It had come with almost unbelievable ferocity. The houses had not been completed when the first hurricanes came, and they were smashed into toothpicks. The winds came, vicious winds full of dust and sleet and ice, wild erratic twisting gales that ripped the village to shreds, tearing off the topsoil that had been broken and fertilized — merciless, never-ending winds that wailed and screamed the planet's protest. The winds drove sand and dirt and ice into the heart of the generators, and the heating units corroded and jammed and went dead. The jeeps and tractors and bulldozers were scored and rusted. The people began dying by the dozens as they huddled down in the pitiful little pits they had dug to try to keep the winds away.

Few of them were still conscious when the Dusties had come silently, in the blizzard, eyes closed tight against the blast, to drag the people up into the hills, into caves and hollows that still showed the fresh marks of carving tools. They had brought food — what kind of food nobody knew, for the colony's food had been destroyed by the first blast of the hurricane — but whatever it was it had kept them alive. And somehow the colonists had survived the winter which seemed never to end. There were frozen legs and ruined eyes; there was pneumonia so swift and virulent that even the antibiotics they managed to salvage could not stop it; there was near starvation — but they were kept alive until the winds began to die, and they walked out of their holes in the ground to see the ruins of their first village.

From that winter on nobody considered the Dusties funny anymore. What had motivated them no one knew, but the colony owed them their lives. The Dusties tried to help the people rebuild. They showed them how to build windshields that would keep houses intact and anchored to the ground when the winds came again. They built little furnaces out of dirt and rock which defied the winds and gave great heat. They showed the colonists a dozen things they needed to know for life on the rugged planet. The colonists in turn tried to teach the Dusties something about Earth and how the colonists had lived and why they had come. But there was a barrier of intelligence that could not be crossed. The Dusties learned simple things, but only slowly and imperfectly. They seemed content to take on their mock overseer's role, moving in and about the village, approving or

"Nobody can get that kind of yield from this planet."

disapproving, but always trying to help. Some became personal pets, though "pet" was the wrong word, because it was more of a strange personal friendship limited by utter lack of communication, than any animal-and-master relationship. The colonists made sure that the Dusties were granted the respect due them as rightful masters of Baron IV. And somehow the Dusties perceived this attitude and were so grateful for the acceptance and friendship that there seemed nothing they wouldn't do for the colonists.

There had been many discussions about them. "You'd think they'd resent our moving in on them," Jack Mario had said one day. "After all, we *are* usurpers. And they treat us like kings. Have you noticed the way they mimic us? I saw one chewing tobacco the other day. He hated the stuff, but he chewed like a trooper."

One of the Dusties had been sitting on Paula's knee when Captain Varga had been talking, and he had known that something was terribly wrong. Now he sat on the desk in the office, moving uneasily back and forth as Paula looked up at Mario's dark face and then across at John Tegan and Mel Dorfman. John's face was dark with anger as he ran his fingers through the heavy gray beard that fell to his chest. Mel sat stunned, shaking his head helplessly. Mario

90

was unable to restrain himself. His face was bitter as he stomped across the room. "But did you see him?" he choked. "Governor of the colony! What does he know about growing *taaro* in this kind of soil?"

The big man looked up, his eyes hollow under craggy brows. "It's below the belt, Paula. But if the government's been overthrown, then the captain is right. It leaves us out on a limb."

Paula shook her head. "I can't give him an answer," she said. "The answer has got to come from the colony. All I can do is speak for the colony."

Tegan stared at the floor. "We're an Earth colony," he said softly. "I know that. I was born in New York. I lived there for many years. But earth isn't my home anymore. This is." He looked at Paula. "I built it, and so did you. All of us built it, even when things were getting stormy back home. Maybe that's why we came, maybe somehow we saw the handwriting on the wall."

"But when did it happen?" Mel burst out suddenly. "How could *anything* so big happen so fast?"

"Speed was the secret," Paula said gloomily. "It was quick, it was well organized, and the government was unstable. We're just caught on the edge of it. Pity the ones living there now. But the new government considers the colonies as areas for exploitation instead of development."

"Well, they can't do it," Mario cried. "This is *our* land, *our* home. Nobody can tell us what to grow in our fields."

"Well, how are you going to stop them?" asked Paula. "The law of the land is sitting out there in that ship. Tomorrow morning he's coming back here to install his little friend as governor. He has guns and soldiers on that ship to back him up. What are you going to do about it?"

"Fight it," Mario said.

"How?"

Jack Mario looked around the room. "There are only a dozen men on that ship," he said softly. "We've got 74. When Varga comes back to the village tomorrow, we tell him to take his friend back to the ship and shove off. We give him five minutes to get turned around, and if he doesn't, we start shooting."

"Just one little thing," said Paula quietly. "What about the supplies? Even if we fought them off and won, what about the food, the clothing, the replacement parts for the machines?''

''We don't need machinery to farm this land,'' said Mario eagerly.. ''There's food here, food we can live on; the Dusties showed us that the first winter. And we can farm the land for our own use and let the machinery rust. There's nothing they can bring us from Earth that we can't do without.''

''We couldn't get away with it!'' Mel Dorfman shook his head bitterly. ''You're asking us to cut ourselves off from Earth completely. But they'd never let us. They'd send ships to bomb us out.''

''We could hide and rebuild after they had finished.''

Paula Farnam sighed. ''They'd never leave us alone, Jack. Didn't you see that captain? His kind of mind can't stand opposition. We'd just be a thorn in the side of the new Earth government. They don't want *any* free colonies.''

''Well, let's give them one.'' Mario sat down tiredly, snapping his fingers at the Dustie. ''Furs!'' he snarled. He looked up, his dark eyes burning. ''It's no good, Paula. We can't let them get away with it. Produce for them, yes. Try to raise the yield for them, yes. But not a governor. If they insist on that we can throw them out.''

''I don't think so. They'd kill every one of us first.''

John Tegan sat up and looked Paula Farnam straight in the eye. ''In that case, Paula, it might just be better if they did.''

Paula stared at him for a moment and slowly stood up. ''All right,'' she said. ''Call a general colony meeting. We'll see what everyone thinks. Then we'll make our plans.''

The ship's jeep skidded to a halt in a cloud of dust. Captain Varga peered through the windshield. Then he stood up, staring at the woman and two men blocking the road at the edge of the village. The little pink-faced man at his side turned white when he saw their faces, and his fingers began to tremble. Each of the three had a gun.

''You'd better clear the road,'' the captain snapped. ''We're driving through.''

Paula Farnam stepped forward. She pointed to Nathan. ''Take your friend there back to the ship. Leave him there. We don't want him here.''

Nathan turned to Varga. ''I told you,'' he said viciously. ''Too big for their boots. Go on through.''

The captain laughed and gunned the motor, started straight for the men blocking the road. Then Jack Mario shot a hole in his front tire. The jeep lurched to a stop. Captain Varga stood up, glaring at the men. "Farnam, step out here," he said.

"You heard us," Paula said, without moving. "Crops, yes. We'll try to increase our yield. But no overseer. Leave him here and we'll kill him."

"Once more," said the captain, "clear the way. This man is your new governor. He will be regarded as the official agent of the earth government until the final production capacity of this colony is determined. Now clear out."

The three didn't move. Without another word, the captain threw the jeep into reverse, jerked back in a curve, and started the jeep, flat tire and all, back toward the ship in a billow of dust.

Abruptly, the village exploded into activity. Four men took up places behind the row of windbreaks beyond the first row of cabins. Paula turned and ran back into the village. She found John Tegan commandeering a squad of ten dirty-faced men. "Are the children all out?" she shouted.

"All taken care of." Tegan spat tobacco juice and wiped his mouth with the back of his hand.

"Where's Mel?"

"Left flank. He'll try to move in behind them. Gonna be tough, Paula. They've got good weapons."

"What about the boys last night?"

John was checking the bolt on his ancient rifle. "Hank and Ringo? Just got back an hour ago. If Varga wants to get his surface planes into action, he's going to have to dismantle them and rebuild them outside. The boys jammed up the launching ports for good." He spat again. "Don't worry, Paula. This is going to be a ground fight."

"Okay." Paula held out her hand to the old man. "This may be it. And if we turn them back, there's bound to be more later."

"There's a lot of planet to hide on," said Tegan. "They may come back, but after a while they'll go again."

Paula nodded. "I just hope we'll still be here when they do."

They waited. It seemed like hours. Paula moved from post to post among the men, heavy-faced men she had known all her life, it seemed. They waited with whatever weapons they had available — pistols, homemade revolvers, ortho-guns, an occasional rifle, even

93

knives and clubs. Paula's heart sank. They were bitter men and women, but they were a mob with no organization, no training for fighting. They would be facing a dozen of Security's best-disciplined shock troops, armed with the latest weapons from Earth's electronics laboratories. The colonists didn't stand a chance.

Paula got her rifle and made her way up the rise of ground overlooking the right flank of the village. Squinting, she could spot the cloud of dust rising up near the glistening ship, moving toward the village. And then, for the first time, she realized that she hadn't seen any Dusties all day.

It puzzled her. They had been in the village in abundance an hour before dawn while the plans were being laid out. She glanced around, hoping to see one of the fuzzy brown forms at her elbow, but she saw nothing. And then, as she stared at the cloud of dust coming across the valley, she thought she saw the ground moving.

She blinked and rubbed her eyes. With a gasp, she dragged out her binoculars and peered down at the valley floor. There were thousands of them, hundreds of thousands, their brown bodies moving slowly out from the hills surrounding the village, converging into a broad, liquid column between the village and the ship. Even as she watched, the column grew thicker, like a heavy blanket being drawn across the road, a multitude of Dusties lining up.

Paula's hair prickled on the back of her neck. They knew so little about the creatures, so *very* little. As she watched the brown carpet rolling out, she tried to think. Could there be a weapon in their hands, could they somehow have perceived the evil that came from the ship, somehow sensed the desperation in the men's voices as they had laid their plans? Paula stared, a sinking feeling in the pit of her stomach. They were there in the road, thousands upon thousands of them, standing there, waiting — for what?

Three columns of dust were coming from the road now. Through the glasses Paula could see the jeeps filled with men in their gleaming gray uniforms, crash helmets tight about their heads, blasters glistening in the pale light. They moved in deadly convoy along the rutted road, closer and closer to the crowd of Dusties overflowing the road.

The Dusties just stood there. They didn't move. They didn't shift or turn. They just waited.

The captain's car was first in line. He pulled up before the line with a screech of brakes, and stared at the sea of creatures before

"The statue was weirdly beautiful."

him. "Get out of there!" he shouted.

The Dusties didn't move.

The captain turned to his men. "Fire into them," he snapped. "Clear a path."

There was a blaze of fire, and a half a dozen Dusties slid to the ground, convulsing. Paula, staring in disbelief, felt a chill pass through her. The Dusties had a weapon, she kept telling herself, they *must* have a weapon, something the colonists had never dreamed of. The guns came up again, and another volley echoed across the valley, and a dozen more Dusties fell to the ground. For every one that fell, another moved stolidly into its place.

With a curse, the captain sat down in the seat, gunned the motor, and started forward. The jeep struck the fallen bodies, rolled over them, and plunged straight into the wall of Dusties. Still they didn't move. The car slowed and stopped, mired down. The other cars picked up momentum and plunged into the brown river of creatures. They too ground to a stop.

The captain started roaring at his men. "Cut them down! We're going to get through here!" Blasters began roaring into the faces of the Dusties, and, as they fell, the jeeps moved forward a few feet

95

until more of the creatures blocked their path.

Paula heard a cry below her and saw Jack Mario standing in the road, gun on the ground, hands out in front of him, staring in horror as the Dusties kept moving into the fire. "Do you see what they're doing!" he screamed. "They'll be slaughtered, every one of them!" And then he was running down the road, shouting at them to stop, and so were Paula and Tegan and the rest of the men and women.

Something hit Paula in the shoulder as she ran. She spun around and fell into the dusty road. A dozen Dusties closed in around her, lifted her up bodily, and started back through the village with her. She tried to struggle, but vaguely she saw that the other men and women were being carried back also while the river of brown creatures held the jeeps at bay. The Dusties were hurrying, half carrying and half dragging her back through the village and up a long ravine into the hills beyond. At last they set Paula on her feet again, plucking urgently at her shirt sleeve as they hurried her along.

She followed them willingly then, with the rest of the colonists at her heels. She didn't know what the Dusties were doing, but she knew they were trying to save her. Finally they reached a cave, a great cleft in the rock that Paula knew for certain had not been there when she had led exploring parties through these hills years before. It was a huge opening, and already a dozen of the men and women were there, waiting, dazed by what they had witnessed down in the valley, while more were stumbling up the rocky incline, tugged along by the fuzzy brown creatures.

Inside the cavern, steps led down the side of the rock, deep into the dark coolness of the earth. Down and down they went, until they suddenly found themselves in a mammoth room lit by blazing torches. Paula stopped and stared at her friends who had already arrived. Jack Mario was sitting on the floor, his face in his hands, sobbing. Tegan was sitting, too, blinking at Paula as if she were a stranger, and Dorfman was trembling like a leaf. Paula stared about her through the dim light, and then looked where Tegan was pointing at the end of the room.

She couldn't see it clearly at first. Finally she made out a raised platform with four steps leading up. A torch lighted either side of a dais at the top, and between the torches, rising high into the gloom, stood a statue.

It was a beautifully carved thing, hewn from the heavy granite that made up the core of this planet, with the same curious styling as other carvings the Dusties had done. The design was intricate, the lines carefully turned and polished. At first Paula thought it was a statue of a Dustie, but when she moved forward and squinted in the dim light, she suddenly realized that it was something else indeed. And in that moment she realized why they were there and why the Dusties had done this incredible thing to protect them.

The statue was weirdly beautiful, the work of a dedicated master sculptor. It was a figure, standing with five-fingered hands on hips, head raised high. Not a portrait, but an image seen through eyes other than human, standing high in the room with the lights burning reverently at its feet.

Unmistakably, it was the statue of a human.

They heard the bombs much later. The granite roof and floor of the cavern trembled, and the men and women stared at each other, helpless and sick as they huddled in that great hall. But presently the bombing stopped. Later, when they stumbled out of that grotto into the late afternoon light, the ship was gone.

They knew it would be back. Possibly it would bring back search parties to hunt down the rebels in the hills; perhaps it would just wait and again bomb out the new village when it rose. But searching parties would never find their quarry, and the village would rise again and again if necessary.

And in the end, somehow, Paula knew that the colonists would find a way to survive here and live free as they had always lived. It might be a bitter struggle, but no matter how hard the fight, there would be one strange and wonderful thing they could count on.

No matter what they had to do, she knew the Dusties would help them.

A CLOSER LOOK

1. What sort of a society do the Dusties seem to have? How did the Earth settlers learn to appreciate it?

2. Why are the Dusties so devoted to the settlers?

3. Do you think that the settlers are right to oppose Varga's orders? Why or why not? What do you think will happen to the settlers in the future?

● May Swenson shows us the earth from the point of view of an alien creature. The alien apparently doesn't know us very well — or perhaps it knows us better than we know ourselves.

May Swenson

SOUTHBOUND ON THE FREEWAY

A tourist came in from Orbitville,
parked in the air, and said:

The creatures of this star
are made of metal and glass.

Through the transparent parts
you can see their guts.

Their feet are round and roll
on diagrams or long

measuring tapes, dark
with white lines.

They have four eyes.
The two in back are red.

Sometimes you can see a five-eyed

one, with a red eye turning

on the top of his head.
He must be special —

the others respect him
and go slow

when he passes, winding
among them from behind.

They all hiss as they glide,
like inches, down the marked

tapes. Those soft shapes,
shadowy inside

the hard bodies — are they
their guts or their brains?

"My first clear thought was of my family."

Whitley Strieber and James Kunetka
WARDAY

● Whitley Streiber writes scripts for horror movies; his friend James Kunetka writes non-fiction books about the scientific research that created atomic bombs. Together, they wrote a book called Warday — their imaginary account of what life in America would be like after a nuclear war. This story is taken from that book. It reads like a non-fiction report for a newspaper, yet it is more horrifying than any monster movie.

NEW YORK, 1998 —
WHITLEY

I was riding a Number 5 bus down Fifth Avenue when the bomb exploded. Of course, I have thought many times about the consequences of the miss. I have wondered what caused it. And I have thought: a nuclear miss doesn't mean much. The city died of it anyway.

The bomb that would have exploded about eight thousand feet directly over my head detonated instead on the eastern edge of Queens.[1]

New York City, October 28, 1998: a clear blue afternoon, just pushing toward five o'clock. While I read the *New York Post* and sucked a Velamint, the world cracked apart. I was sitting in the bus, just behind the rear exit door. I remember that it was one of the GM buses, with the darkly tinted windows. All of a sudden it was lit up inside with a chalky brilliance. A strange and unpleasantly hot light penetrated everything.

Sudden darkness followed — because our eyes, of course, were stunned by the intensity of the flash. The driver shouted and stopped the bus. I just sat there. We all did. We couldn't see a thing. I heard a horn honking.

Then the blast hit. There was no warning, just a sudden cataract[2] of sound and wind. The bus rocked violently. There were deep thuds and shattering noises as pieces of roofing and glass came down. The noise rose and rose until I thought it would never stop. People were trying to get out of the bus. I crouched down on the floor. My heart was pounding; I was gasping. I had my eyes shut tight. At that moment I was thinking in terms of a terrorist attack or maybe of the electric plant in the East Thirties blowing up. The thought of a nuclear bomb didn't occur to me until the noise subsided[3] and my eyesight got back to normal. Then I looked out.

The chaos was so great that my mind simply went blank. The images swept all thought away. Windows were broken, cars were up on the sidewalk, and people were running, staggering, lying in the street. A dark yellow haze of dust cast everything in eerie light.

My first clear thought was of my family. My son was in the third grade at Grace Church School and taking an after-school gymnastics class. As far as I knew, my wife was at home. I thought I'd better call her and tell her that there had been some kind of an explosion, but that I was all right and not to worry. By this time the driver had gotten the doors open. He was trying to restart the bus and not getting anywhere at all. Of course, we didn't know a single thing about electromagnetic pulse back then. He had no idea that the bus' electronic ignition had been destroyed.

Because the bus was broken down, the driver gave us all transfers, and we filed off. Suddenly all I could think about was my boy. I started off down Fifth Avenue at a trot. People were lying everywhere, in every condition. Lots of them were bloody from flying glass, many more discolored by flash burns. I did not know it, but I was bleeding, too. The blood ran down my neck and soaked my shirt like sweat. I'd had a slice taken out of my scalp that I wouldn't feel until much later.

I saw gangs of kids coming out of the Fourteenth Street stores with everything you could name in their hands: radios, records, clothes, candy bars. They were laughing and shrieking.

My mind was still far from clear. I just couldn't seem to grasp what had happened. There was no reason to think that there had been a nuclear attack, though I kept considering and then rejecting that thought. U.S.-Soviet tensions weren't high. There'd been no sign of conflict, none at all.

It was the sky over Queens and Brooklyn that made me think of a nuclear bomb. Through the dusty air I could see ash-black clouds shot through with long red flames. These clouds were immense. They stretched up and up until they were lost in their own expanding billows.[4] There was no impression of a mushroom cloud, but I knew that was what it was, a mushroom cloud seen so close that it didn't look like a mushroom. The coldest, most awful dread I have ever known came upon me then.

I knew it for certain: a nuclear device had been exploded at the eastern edge of the city. I thought, the lives! Later it was estimated that a million people had died in the instant of the explosion. Hundreds of thousands more were dying right now.

I was walking on a grate above the Fourteenth Street subway station when a blast of dirty air from below practically blew me off my feet. It was accompanied by the most horrible screaming I have ever heard, then the nasty bellow of water. Though nobody knew it then, the tidal wave caused by the bombs that had detonated at sea had arrived and was filling the subway system. Those screams still come to me in the night.

I found the school closed and locked. There were lots of broken windows, but the lower floors were barred. I shouted, and the Latin teacher opened the front door for me. Inside, the kids were sitting quietly in the great hall with their teachers. "What's going on?" Mr. Lewis asked me. "I think we've been hit by an atomic bomb," I replied. He nodded. "We all think that."

I went to my boy. He jumped up and flew into my arms, and then started screaming because he saw all the blood on my back. The school nurse came over to tend the wound. She said I needed at least five stitches. But what could we do? I ended up with a brushing of Betadine and bandage.

The phones weren't working, so I couldn't call my wife Anne. It was then that I made the decision that saved my life.

I didn't know it at the time, but like all people caught outside during the initial stages of the disaster, I had received a radiation dose. If I had gone out even another fifteen minutes at the height of the fallout period, I would have died. What kept me from doing so was my belief that my wife's instinct would also be to come to the school and I was more likely to find her by waiting than by searching.

Not ten minutes later she appeared. She was wearing my felt hat and carrying an umbrella. I will never forget how it felt to kiss her at that moment, to feel her in my arms. And then Andrew said, "Let's have a family hug." We held each other, and I told them both what I thought had happened.

Other parents were now arriving at the school. We moved the children into the gym, which had no windows. We decided to make that a shelter for all the families who wanted to stay. Anne and I went to the locker room and took long showers. Some of the parents who did not take this precaution died in days. Others were unaffected. For the most part, it depended on how long they had been outside, and whether or not they had been shielded from the initial burst of gamma rays from the blast.

We had the church right there, of course, attached to the school. Grace is probably New York City's most beautiful church, and it served us well in the next few days. It could be reached from the school without going outside. While the city died, we prayed there. At that time I wondered if humanity would triumph. Despite what was happening, I found myself trusting the goodness in us more than hating the violence. I still feel that way.

By now it had occurred to us that there must be dangerous radiation. We were trying to keep trips outside to a minimum, and had hung blankets over the windows.

Two of our group went to the roof to put out any fires that might start there. They held plastic dropcloths from the art room over their heads as protection from cinders and radiation. The fallout worried us even more than the fire. We knew little about it. Was there still too much radiation in the air, or should we join the exodus[5] west instead of trying to fight the fire? We just couldn't recall. On balance, most of us decided to remain at the school a little longer. At least we were reasonably safe there for the time being. We also had light from church candles, food from the school's kitchen, and water from the tower, which we hoped wasn't contaminated by radiation. Anne and Andrew and I decided that we would remain inside this building, away from the windows, for as long as we could. We did not know then that the hot cloud from Washington was on its way up the seaboard, spreading extinction. If we had tried to leave then, we would have been caught in it with the millions whose footsteps still had not stopped.

More than from the lack of water and power, people were scared because of the lack of news. Those who had gone as far east as the river confirmed that there was a holocaust[6] going on in Brooklyn and Queens. They had been able to feel the heat on their faces even on this side of the river, and the wind being pulled into the fire was still strong enough to make it hard to stand up. People reported that the fire made a great hissing roar. They described it as sounding like a railroad train, a hurricane, or the voice of an angry crowd.

The vast majority of electronic devices — computers, televisions, radios, microwave stations, radar, electronic car ignitions — had been shorted out by Soviet bombs detonated in outer space. The explosions had been invisible and had had no effect except to blanket the country with a brief, massive burst of electromagnetic energy.

Because of the electromagnetic pulse, we had no access to broadcast news.

I will never forget the moment when somebody outside started yelling about *The New York Times*. The next thing I knew, there was a man coming in with a paper. It was the famous sixteen-page extra, which was the last news we were to see for a long time. I still don't know how the *Times* managed to get that paper out. Someone told me it was produced in New Jersey before local electric power was lost.

I remember the headline:

NUCLEAR ATTACK
BY AT LEAST THREE MISSILES
DEVASTATES CITY

And the lead story: "Nuclear weapons detonated over Queens and Brooklyn on October 28 at approximately 4:45 p.m., causing catastrophic devastation and leaving both boroughs in a flaming ruins. An estimated two million people lost their lives."

It was there also that we read of Washington. We were stunned, confused. Washington no longer existed. There was no President, no Vice-President, no Congress, nobody. We had no government.

"Washington, D.C., the seat of government of the United States of America since 1800, has been destroyed by a surprise nuclear attack. Reports from the area indicate catastrophic destruction on a scale previously unknown in human affairs. The city was swept away in a sea of fire. Not a building remains standing, not a monument intact. Observers are unable even to approach within ten miles of the city. Baltimore, Maryland, is also burning, as are the majority of smaller communities surrounding the District of Columbia." It went on, but I find that my memory does not serve me to quote the rest.

Until that moment I hadn't thought beyond the immediate situation: how to live through the next few hours, and would I come down with radiation sickness? Every passing moment of queasiness or faint chill was terrifying. We had set up a hospital in the parents' lounge. There we attended the sick and dying as best we could. The school's science teacher, Mrs. Dannay, had managed to rig up a thing called a Kearney Fallout Meter, and was busy dividing the school into safe and unsafe areas.

The KFM was made in a Folger's coffee can and consisted of two leaves of aluminum foil hung side by side on strings inside the can. It was covered by the clear plastic top from a Tupperware container in which the fourth grade had been hatching frog eggs. The bottom of the can held crushed gypsum. This was used as a drying agent because humidity can affect the ability of the foil strips to respond to the presence of radiation. Mrs. Dannay had dug the gypsum out of the wall in the lab. It was just ordinary wallboard.

She could tell by the way the leaves of foil spread apart or came together how much gamma radiation was present in a given area. It wasn't accurate enough to measure hot spots on people, but it did help us to confirm that our water was not highly contaminated and that our top two floors and the area of the church closest to the main doors were, as well as all areas on the main floor of the school near doors and windows, and the whole central foyer.

That Kearney Fallout Meter probably saved the lives of most of the people in our school. It also enabled Mrs. Dannay to develop a rough estimate of radiation outside. She told us that trips out were safe only for fifteen or twenty minutes, and that no individual should make more than one trip.

It was on the third day that I began to have symptoms. My head had become infected despite frequent applications of Betadine and plenty of soap and water. Of course, I had been exposed to radiation and that had lowered my resistance to disease.

My head hurt terribly. When I started vomiting, Anne and Andrew took me off to a corner of the hall and tended me there. They did not want to put me in the parents' lounge, which had become a virtual dying room. Just about everybody who went in there died within a few hours. Of course, people had no notion of how to protect themselves from radiation, and many of them had gotten very severe doses. I hoped that my dose wasn't too terrible, but I also suspected that combined with the head wound and the rough conditions, it might weaken me enough to threaten my life.

We prayed a good deal. Since Warday my faith has become so essential to me that I can hardly imagine being without it. When I thought I was dying, I began to pray, as I had prayed in times of childhood crisis. I was not afraid to die, but I felt awful that I must leave Anne and Andrew.

By this time Dr. Leo Stein had arrived. He treated me with ampicillin for my infection, then dressed the head wound. Nine days after Warday I was on my feet again. I weighed a hundred and thirty-one pounds. In nine days I had lost forty-six pounds.

Since then, my lifedose level has been diagnosed as terminal,[7] so I am waiting for the outbreak of cancer. It could start tomorrow, or next year, or in five years. It might never start, but the odds in favor of that are very small.

By the time I recovered, the radiation level in the streets was not detectable on our Kearney Fallout Meter. Our food supplies were dwindling, and water was strictly rationed. About a third of the families had left the school.

On November 6, 1998, Anne and Andrew and I started out on our own journey home. It was to be a long and bitter trip, ending in sorrow.

Home is where one's family lives. For Anne and Andrew and me, this was San Antonio. Not until ten hard days of traveling, when we were on a bus in Arkansas, did we learn that it had suffered the same fate as Washington and was no more.

DALLAS, 2003 —
JIM

I was forty-nine when I left with Whitley on an adventure through

"We have been married for twenty-three years."

postwar America. I was very aware that the five years that had just passed had been the equivalent of at least twenty prewar years. I kept wondering how many more I would use up on the journey.

And I wonder now how many are left.

When Whitley and I first considered writing this book, my impulse was to stay right here at home in Dallas and cling to what life I have left. But then I began to wonder: What is the country actually *like* now? Everything certainly seems different. If there has been fundamental change, is it productive?

I live in a nice house with two others; I own a fairly good car. I cherish my safety passionately. On Warday both my wife and my mother disappeared. My mother was in the maelstrom[8] of San Antonio, my wife was in Austin. Mother, I know, is dead. But my wife — there is always the chance she remains alive, caught in the great shuffling departures that have marked the famine and the flu. I wrote only my mother's name in the Governor's *Book of the Dead*.

I ate dandelion leaves during the famine. I know what it is to have the flu and get told to leave the hospital or face arrest. I know what it is to lose relatives, home, possessions, friends. And I know how I feel when I watch the sunset over the roofs of the neighborhood and hear the snick of the scythe[9] as my neighbor cuts his lawn. But the things I did not know seemed to me more important. What, for example, was life like in the least affected parts of the country, such as California? How was the federal government functioning now, with its new capital in Los Angeles and a whole new breed of bureaucrats?[10]

Curiosity became interest and I found myself drawn into working on the book. We both knew it couldn't be done from Dallas, and that we would have to do our research by traveling, talking with people, getting in touch with the landscape, gathering the important personal stories and sensations even more than the official facts.

We made phone calls and sent letters. The telephone system is unpredictable. Some large areas are still completely without service. Others were never affected at all. To find out if a place has service, it is easiest just to call. Austin, Texas, is as easy to reach as ever. A call to Los Angeles was interrupted by an operator asking us to state our business — our first taste of California's raging fear of outsiders.

When you call San Antonio, a recorded voice says, "We're sorry, but the number you have called does not exist in the 512 area code. Please consult your directory and try again."

Each regional telephone company has dealt with its destroyed areas in different ways. Call Cheyenne, Wyoming, and you'll get an announcement that the number has been disconnected. New York clicks on the third ring, and returns silence.

DALLAS — WHITLEY

It is a bright August morning. The air is dense and full of the smell of the wisteria that grows around our back door. I have been up since five-thirty, watching the sky go from gold to white.

Anne has given me a breakfast of eggs and a glass of goat's milk. Our eggs are small and brown, from our own bantam hens. Good town birds. The goat's milk is from the Perrys, across the street. Their son Robert keeps three goats. On the table there are hard, sour grapes from our vines.

Anne sits across from me, her chin in her hands. We have been married for twenty-three years. We know that our remaining time together is quite limited, and so she sees my journey as a family

"We have always hugged like this, the three of us."

tragedy. But she understands my motives. I was a writer for many years, and I did not voluntarily give that up. Anne will not stop me from doing something of real value with my skill.

"You've got a dozen hardboiled eggs in your backpack," Anne says. "It's all I could get out of the hens."

"It's a lot."

"I made some bread." She hands me a loaf, and my heart almost breaks. Flour is hard to get these days, and she must have hoarded this carefully. It's quite a surprise.

Andrew, my tall, lean, thirteen-year-old son, is looking at me. Our eyes meet. For a moment he is grave, his face full of tension. "Good luck, Dad," he says. We have talked at length about my journey, and he approves. He also knows the risks. "I'll take care of Mom," he says. "I can do it." I believe that. At the age of ten, this young man kept his head about him when he was starving. He organized midnight trips to abandoned warehouses, learned at the library how to recognize edible plants, and never spoke a word of complaint through all those terrible months. At twelve he helped on a disinfecting crew during the flu. He then faced that disease himself, and lay in this very house between life and death. "What happens, happens," he said then. "I know that God'll keep me."

There is a sound of footsteps outside, and Jim Kunetka comes in the back door. He is blade-thin, smiling, looking rather worn. When I ask if he slept last night, he only smiles more. Anne gives him oatmeal and grapes, and he eats eagerly. He has been my friend since we were children. Lately he has been working as a journalist, while I have gone into microfarming and indoor garden design. I can build you a hydroponic[11] garden sufficient to supply a family of four with vegetables year-round, and locate it indoors so you don't have to worry about fallout. Before the war I was a middle-range novelist. We were happy and fat then. My horror stories were successful, because happy people crave the luxury of artificial fear. I wouldn't write one now — the very idea is loathsome.

"Our appointment is at eight-thirty," Jim says in his most brisk manner.

I swallow the last of my milk and get up. Anne and Andrew and I hold each other for a moment. Our faces are touching; our arms are around one another's shoulders. We have always hugged like this, the three of us. For me it is a symbol of our endurance as a family and as civilized people, and of the truth of our love.

LOS ANGELES —
WHITLEY

The old train clicks along the tracks. Jim and I are sitting in the observation car, staring out the wide picture windows at the desert. I haven't been to Los Angeles since 1993.

I know a few things about L.A. First, with nearly nine million residents, it is by far the most populous city in the United States. Despite the general population decline, it has grown by nearly a million since 1998. It is more than four times the size of the second largest city, San Francisco, and larger than New York was before the war.

The conductor comes through calling, "Needles, next stop Needles." There is stirring in the car. Needles is one of California's ports of entry. To get into the state, you've got to show twenty gold dollars or an equivalent amount in goods or paper currency, and a valid entry permit. The only way to get such a permit is to have business in the state or a job waiting for you there.

"Needles," the conductor shouts. "Everybody stay in the train, stay in the train!"

We slow to a crawl and draw up to the platform. I'm shocked. There are soldiers armed with submachine guns every fifteen feet. Behind them are huge signs:

ILLEGAL ALIENS
LIABLE TO BE SHOT.

An amplified voice can be heard: "Do not leave the train. Have your entry permits ready. Do not leave the train."

California State Police officers in white crash helmets, face masks, black leather boots, and khaki uniforms come across the platform in formation. They carry pistols in holsters. At a barked order, half of them draw their weapons. The other half have clipboards. These are some of California's famous Processing Officers.

Suddenly a man in full radiation gear comes into the car from the side opposite the platform. He is carrying a small black device with a digital readout. It has a long, thin probe attached. He waves it back and forth as he moves down the aisle. He touches some of the passengers with it, and inserts it down the collars of others. He

"Do not leave the train. Have your entry permits ready."

squirts a bright red aerosol on the back of one man's hand, and tells him that he's got to go take a detox[12] shower and get an issue of paper clothing before he can even get port-of-entry processing.

Jim and I are examined without comment. Apparently this device only measures present radiation. My high lifedose is still my own business.

Los Angeles is the greatest city in the United States. In size, San Francisco isn't even close.

There are things here from the past, but there is something from the present that is missing. It is the sense of having suffered — the subtle tension that hangs, everywhere else we have been, between friends and strangers alike. California didn't suffer too much from the famine, and few people here were weak enough to be killed by the Cincinnati Flu. Radiation sickness is almost unknown, except among refugees.

On our first night in the bright streets of Los Angeles, I find myself returning to my old city habits, moving with quick anonymity[13] and never meeting anybody else's eyes.

There is a much stronger Japanese influence than ever before. The streets are packed not only with Japanese businessmen but also with clerks and factory workers and children with American nannies. And there are cars: new Nissans that whistle when they accelerate and get 130 miles to a gallon of gas, sporty Toyota Z-90s, Isuzus, Mitsubishis and the occasional Mercedes-Benz.

More, though, than its prosperity, L.A. has the feeling of prewar America. It has the cheer and the confidence that one associates with former days.

I indulge[14] myself shamelessly. In Little Tokyo there are dozens of open-air fruit and vegetable stands where melons and tomatoes and lettuce and carrots and squash and dozens of other things are stacked in abundance. Little Tokyo, by the way, now extends all the way to Sixth Street. It must be four times its prewar size. In Little Tokyo I buy an enormous vine-ripened tomato for two cents and eat it like an apple. I have not eaten such a thing in years. It is rich beyond belief, dense with a flavor that sweeps through my nostrils, heavy with juice.

LOS ANGELES — JIM

I am dazed by California. Sometimes, walking the streets, I get a joy in me, and I think to myself that the past is returning like a tide, and soon all will again be well. There is energy and movement here — danger too, of course — but there is a little of something else that I think is also an important part of the American spirit — frivolity.[15] Not much, I'll grant you, but it isn't dead yet.

Of course, the place is also tension-ridden. The Americans who are here illegally are considered criminals, and are cruelly exploited.[16] The division between rich and poor is very sharp. Beverly Hills and Nob Hill glitter with Rolls-Royces and Mercedes-Benzes.

Californians consider the rest of the United States as a foreign country that is poverty-stricken and potentially dangerous. The local press reports it only on occasion. A bus plunge killing a hundred in Illinois will appear on the bottom of page forty of the *Los Angeles Times*. The same paper will headline the discovery of strontium 90[17] in Anaheim.

In California, more than anywhere else, you hear talk of dividing the United States. "California First" and "Forget the Rest" are common T-shirt slogans.

"Venders commonly advertise their fruit as 'radiation-free.' "

There is also a lot of radiation fear. Vendors commonly advertise their fruits as "radiation-free." There are walk-in clinics where for fifteen cents you can get a whole-body scan or have objects checked. The government regularly warns people to avoid the black market because of the danger of contaminated goods from "abroad" — which must mean the rest of the United States.

[After leaving California, Jim and Whitley travel by train and bus back across America. They go through Denver, Kansas City, Cleveland, Pittsburgh, and on to Philadelphia. — Ed.]

PHILADELPHIA —
WHITLEY

Thirteenth Street Station in Philadelphia was an astonishing sight as we walked in, weary from the long bus ride. We were planning to catch the train to Meridian, Mississippi, and from there to take the bus to Dallas.

There must have been a thousand children in the station. They were all quiet and sat in rows on the floor. Here and there, one slept

115

in another's lap. Older kids took care of babies. The cries of babies echoed in the huge waiting room. A supervisor moved among the rows.

There was none of the hubbub[18] of childhood among these kids. Their situation was serious, and they knew it.

We did not speak, not until long afterward, when we were on the train. The children were jammed into eight passenger cars behind us. We were in the through-car. Ahead of us were three ''state cars'' for people planning to leave the train in resident-only states, such as Georgia, the Carolinas, and Virginia.

We wanted to find out about the kids and started moving back toward their cars. When we opened the door we saw dim lights and hard seats, and smelled their odor again. These were not the normal Amtrak cars, but old commuters with ceiling fans and dim bulbs. They were obviously put on at the last moment. They rattled and swayed. The night wind bellowed in the windows. The trainmen were giving out blankets and sheets, which the children made into beds on the seats and the floor. There was a seriousness among them that was deeply disturbing. It was as if this bedmaking were the most important thing in the world and these blankets were valuable beyond price.

Jim found one of the adult supervisors at the rear of the car. She could have been thirty years old, or fifty; it was hard to tell. A little boy slept with his head in her lap, a girl of twelve with her head on her shoulder. She held a baby in her arms. Another baby lay in the girl's arms. ''We're writing a book,'' Jim said. ''May we talk to you?''

She smiled. ''I guess so, if you don't wake anybody up. I've got some mighty tired kids on this train.''

''How did you get your job?''

''Well, I have my Master's in early-childhood education, and I have a degree in child psychology. But I didn't get the job on qualifications. I was with the State Department of Social Work before the war. Afterward, we found ourselves with tremendous numbers of orphans. It was natural that anybody in the Welfare Department who knew anything at all about kids, or who just liked them, would end up doing what I'm doing.''

''Why are they on the train?''

She smiled again. ''These children are being transferred to an institution in Alabama. We've been informed by the Department of

Agriculture that there's going to be another grain emergency by April, so we're evacuating them to a better-fed area. We do not want to go through another famine the way we went through the last one. My unit buried an awful lot of children. That will not happen again, not if there is any way to prevent it.''

We returned to our own car.

I closed my eyes. Music came into my mind, soft and slow. It was the music of the swaying car and the dark. It reminded me of my own life as a child.

DALLAS, OCT. 10, 2003, 2:15 A.M. — WHITLEY

I am home again, sitting at the kitchen table with my notebook and a fresh pencil. It is two o'clock in the morning. I arrived home at nine, but so far I haven't been able to sleep.

Being on the road so long has made me sharply aware of ordinary household things: the refrigerator's humming, the kitchen clock's ticking. Through the window above the sink I can see the moon hanging low in the sky. The night is rich and warm and fills me with expectancy.[19] There is a faint smell of flowers on the air.

A mockingbird sings, leaves rustle. How fine a moment the world can yet make! We have been in shattered years, but there is peace in our minds now.

We are not like we were before. Now our habit is more often to accept and heal rather than to reject and punish.

It was nearly midnight when we went to bed. I do not think I have ever felt anything as good as lying down beside my wife in the dark and feeling the softness and warmth of her.

I expected to fall into deep black sleep, but I did not. The voices of the road came back to me. All the words came back at once, softly, persistently.

I got up and stood looking long at the shadow of my wife in our bed. I was filled with an emotion so rich that it hurt. I went past my son's room, listened to his heavy sleep, and then came down here to try to write this last little bit.

I suppose the world is passing through a thundering moment of history.

The ''U.S.'' and the ''USSR'' I grew up with are gone, and that is strange. It is, I suppose, also history. If we could have our old

America back, I suspect that most of us would gladly take the old Soviet Union, too. We could live so well together, in the calm of present maturity.

Looking back, the war seems odd and exotic.[20] It's as if it were fought not by us, but by innocent people who were disguised as ourselves — people who, in their fury, forgot how fragile we were. It is eerie to remember the bitter hatred I felt against the Russians when they shot down that Korean airliner in '83, or after the Kabul firebombing in '86. Those brutal acts seemed the work of pride, but time and experience have revealed that they were the fearful doings of the trapped. I wish we could reach back through time and heal our relationship.

But what that past world might or might not have done matters little now.

I think much more of healing my own body. I touch my hands to my face, and run my fingers over the wrinkles that complicate my cheeks.

These are the hands and this is the face of a Warday casualty. I wonder what is going wrong in the depths of my body, in among the pulsing organs and the blood. Are there cells that should not be there, stubborn and growing in the softness of me?

I want to die right here in this house, attended by my wife and son. Even if I must feel pain, I will not choose euthanasia.[21] I want my pain. Perhaps that is a silly and old-fashioned notion, but I do not recall giving myself life and feel uneasy about taking it from myself.

I look down at the table and listen to my pencil scratching along the pad. Lord, heal me. Heal my world. Heal the past. If we could accept one another so completely that we were free of all judgment, of all anger, of all denial, would heaven not shine through?

Nuclear weapons were the clearest symptom of what was out of balance about the past. Two societies were so interested in their differences that they came to hate their common ground. That obsession was as a cancer in the mind and heart of the old world. It spread cruelty and blindness through the whole enormous body, and finally killed it.

Now I am going upstairs. I'll finish these last few lines in bed.

As I slip into our room, I see that Anne is sleeping heavily. I get in beside her. There is a sense of completion now. At last I am going to sleep.

I lie down, drawing the sheet up around my chin. Music comes to me, an unknown melody, and an image of my son rises in my mind. I want to allow myself to have hope for him and his generation.

If only we have gained wisdom from the fire. If only we can accept how alike we all are, one and another.

[1] **Queens:** one of the five boroughs of New York City; Whitley is in the borough of Manhattan when the bomb explodes
[2] **cataract:** downpour; flood
[3] **subsided:** became quiet or less
[4] **billows:** waves
[5] **exodus:** mass departure
[6] **holocaust:** great fiery destruction
[7] **terminal:** resulting in eventual death
[8] **maelstrom:** a powerful disturbance, like a whirlpool sucking in everything
[9] **scythe:** a tool with a long curved blade used for cutting grass by hand
[10] **bureaucrats:** government officials
[11] **hydroponic:** growth of plants in chemical solutions with or without soil
[12] **detox:** detoxification
[13] **anonymity:** having no known name or identity
[14] **indulge:** gratify
[15] **frivolity:** joy; lightness of spirit
[16] **exploited:** taken advantage of
[17] **strontium 90:** hazardous material present in nuclear fallout
[18] **hubbub:** noise; confusion
[19] **expectancy:** the state of looking forward to something
[20] **exotic:** foreign; alien; unusual
[21] **euthanasia:** mercy killing

A CLOSER LOOK

1. How does the war change life in America? Why do Whitley and Jim decide to travel around the country?

2. What do Whitley and Jim like about California after the war? What don't they like about California after the war?

3. What does Whitley mean when he says, "If only we have gained wisdom from the fire"? How do you think nuclear war could be avoided?

• Jeffers lived earlier in this century on California's beautiful Monterey Peninsula. The scenery was still unspoiled then, but the land was being developed and crowds of people were pouring in. As he faced this future, he regretted the destruction of so much wilderness. What, he wondered, would survive?

Robinson Jeffers

HARDER THAN GRANITE

It is a pity the shock-waves
Of the present population-explosion must push in here too.
They will certainly within a century
Eat up the old woods I planted and throw down my stonework: Only
    the little tower,
Four-foot-thick-walled and useless, may stand for a time.
That and some verses. It is curious that flower-soft verse
Is sometimes harder than granite, tougher than a steel cable, more
    alive than life.

"It's someone's test satellite — "

Arthur C. Clarke

WHO'S THERE?

● What sort of people will live and work in space? Will they be fearless, romantic, comic-book characters, engaged in life-and-death struggles against alien forces? More than likely, they will be cut from the same ordinary mold as ourselves. In this story, the author of the science fiction classic 2001: A Space Odyssey imagines a time when life in space is as routine as life on Earth — until the day something unexpected happens.

WHEN SATELLITE CONTROL CALLED ME, I WAS writing up the day's progress report in the Observation Bubble — the glass-domed office that juts out from the axis of the space station like the hubcap of a wheel. It was not really a good place to work, for the view was too overwhelming. Only a few yards away I could see the construction teams performing their slow-motion ballet as they put the station together like a giant jigsaw puzzle. And beyond them, twenty thousand miles below, was the blue-green glory of the full Earth, floating against the raveled star clouds of the Milky Way.

"Station Supervisor here," I answered. "What's the trouble?"

"Our radar's showing a small echo two miles away, almost stationary, about five degrees west of Sirius. Can you give us a visual report on it?"

Anything matching our orbit so precisely could hardly be a meteor; it would have to be something we'd dropped — perhaps an inadequately secured piece of equipment that had drifted away from the station. So I assumed; but when I pulled out my binoculars and searched the sky around Orion, I soon found my mistake. Though this space traveler was man-made, it had nothing to do with us.

"I've found it," I told Control. "It's someone's test satellite — cone-shaped, four antennas, and what looks like a lens system in its base. Probably U.S. Air Force, early nineteen-sixties, judging by the design. I know they lost track of several when their transmitters failed. There were quite a few attempts to hit this orbit before they finally made it."

After a brief search through the files, Control was able to confirm my guess. It took a little longer to find out that Washington wasn't in the least bit interested in our discovery of a twenty-year-old stray satellite, and would be just as happy if we lost it again.

"Well, we can't do *that*," said Control. "Even if nobody wants it, the thing's a menace to navigation. Someone had better go out and haul it aboard."

That someone, I realized, would have to be me. I dared not detach a man from the closely knit construction teams, for we were already behind schedule — and a single day's delay on this job cost a million dollars. All the radio and TV networks on Earth were waiting impatiently for the moment when they could route their programs through us, and thus provide the first truly global service, spanning the world from Pole to Pole.

"I'll go out and get it," I answered, snapping an elastic band over my papers so that the air currents from the ventilators wouldn't set them wandering around the room. Though I tried to sound as if I was doing everyone a great favor, I was secretly not at all displeased. It had been at least two weeks since I'd been outside; I was getting a little tired of schedules, maintenance reports, and all the glamorous ingredients of a Space Station Supervisor's life.

The only member of the staff I passed on my way to the air lock was Tommy, our recently acquired cat. Pets mean a great deal to men thousands of miles from Earth, but there are not many animals that can adapt themselves to a weightless environment. Tommy mewed plaintively[1] at me as I clambered into my space suit, but I was in too much of a hurry to play with him.

At this point, perhaps I should remind you that the suits we use on the station are completely different from the flexible affairs men wear when they want to walk around on the Moon. Ours are really baby spaceships, just big enough to hold one man. They are stubby

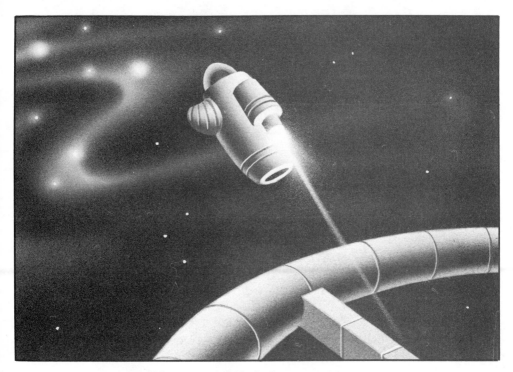

"Ours are really baby spaceships."

cylinders, about seven feet long, fitted with low-powered propulsion jets, and have a pair of accordion-like sleeves at the upper end for the operator's arms. Normally, however, you keep your hands drawn inside the suit, working the manual controls in front of your chest.

As soon as I'd settled down inside my very exclusive spacecraft, I switched on power and checked the gauges on the tiny instrument panel. There's a magic word, "FORB," that you'll often hear spacemen mutter as they climb into their suits; it reminds them to test fuel, oxygen, radio, batteries. All my needles were well in the safety zone, so I lowered the transparent hemisphere over my head and sealed myself in. For a short trip like this, I did not bother to check the suit's internal lockers, which were used to carry food and special equipment for extended missions.

As the conveyor belt decanted[2] me into the air lock, I felt like an Indian papoose being carried along on its mother's back. Then the pumps brought the pressure down to zero, the outer door opened, and the last traces of air swept me out into the stars, turning very slowly head over heels.

The station was only a dozen feet away, yet I was now an

independent planet — a little world of my own. I was sealed up in a tiny, mobile cylinder, with a superb view of the entire Universe, but I had practically no freedom of movement inside the suit. The padded seat and safety belts prevented me from turning around, though I could reach all the controls and lockers with my hands or feet.

In space, the great enemy is the sun, which can blast you to blindness in seconds. Very cautiously, I opened up the dark filters on the "night" side of my suit, and turned my head to look out at the stars. At the same time I switched the helmet's external sunshade to automatic, so that whichever way the suit gyrated my eyes would be shielded from that intolerable glare.

Presently, I found my target — a bright fleck of silver whose metallic glint distinguished it clearly from the surrounding stars. I stamped on the jet-control pedal, and felt the mild surge of acceleration as the low-powered rockets sent me moving away from the station. After ten seconds of steady thrust, I estimated that my speed was great enough, and cut off the drive. It would take me five minutes to coast the rest of the way, and not much longer to return with my salvage.

And it was at that moment, as I launched myself out into the abyss, that I knew that something was horribly wrong.

It is never completely silent inside a space suit; you can always hear the gentle hiss of oxygen, the faint whirr of fans and motors, the susurration[3] of your own breathing — even, if you listen carefully enough, the rhythmic thump that is the pounding of your heart. These sounds reverberate through the suit, unable to escape into the surrounding void; they are the unnoticed background of life in space, for you are aware of them only when they change.

They had changed now; to them had been added a sound which I could not identify. It was an intermittent, muffled thudding, sometimes accompanied by a scraping noise, as of metal upon metal.

I froze instantly, holding my breath and trying to locate the alien sound with my ears. The meters on the control board gave no clues; all the needles were rock-steady on their scales, and there were none of the flickering red lights that would warn of impending disaster. That was some comfort, but not much. I had long ago learned to trust my instincts in such matters; their alarm signals were flashing now, telling me to return to the station before it was too late .

Even now, I do not like to recall those next few minutes, as panic

"Panic slowly flooded into my mind like a rising tide."

slowly flooded into my mind like a rising tide, overwhelming the dams of reason and logic which every man must erect against the mystery of the Universe. I knew then what it was like to face insanity; no other explanation fitted the facts.

For it was no longer possible to pretend that the noise disturbing me was that of some faulty mechanism. Though I was in utter isolation, far from any other human being or indeed any material object, I was not alone. The soundless void was bringing to my ears the faint but unmistakable stirrings of life.

In that first, heart-freezing moment it seemed that something was trying to get into my suit — something invisible, seeking shelter from the cruel and pitiless vacuum of space. I whirled madly in my harness, scanning the entire sphere of vision around me except for the blazing, forbidden cone toward the sun. There was nothing there, of course. There could not be — yet that purposeful scrabbling was clearer than ever.

Despite the nonsense that has been written about us, it is not true that spacemen are superstitious. But can you blame me if, as I came to the end of logic's resources, I suddenly remembered how Bernie Sumers had died, no farther from the station than I was?

It was one of those "impossible" accidents; it always is. Three things had gone wrong at once. Bernie's oxygen regulator had run wild and set the pressure soaring, the safety valve had failed to blow — and a faulty joint had given way instead. In a fraction of a second, his suit was open to space.

I had never known Bernie, but suddenly his fate became of overwhelming importance to me — for a horrible idea had come into my mind. One does not talk about these things, but a damaged space suit is too valuable to be thrown away, even if it has killed its wearer. It is repaired, renumbered — and issued to someone else.

What happens to the soul of a man who dies between the stars, far from his native world? Are you still here, Bernie, clinging to the last object that linked you to your lost and distant home?

As I fought the nightmares that were swirling around me — for now it seemed that the scratchings and soft fumblings were coming from all directions — there was one last hope to which I clung. For the sake of my sanity, I had to prove that this wasn't Bernie's suit — that the metal walls so closely wrapped around me had never been another man's coffin.

It took me several tries before I could press the right button and switch my transmitter to the emergency wavelength. "Station!" I gasped. "I'm in trouble! Get records to check my suit history and — "

I never finished; they say my yell wrecked the microphone. But what man alone in the absolute isolation of a space suit would *not* have yelled when something patted him softly on the back of the neck?

I must have lunged forward, despite the safety harness, and smashed against the upper edge of the control panel. When the rescue squad reached me a few minutes later, I was still unconscious, with an angry bruise across my forehead.

And so I was the last person in the whole satellite relay system to know what had happened. When I came to my senses an hour later, all our medical staff was gathered around my bed, but it was quite a while before the doctors bothered to look at me. They were much too busy playing with the three cute little kittens our badly misnamed Tommy had been rearing in the seclusion of my space suit's Number Five Storage Locker.

[1] **plaintively:** with an expression of sadness or suffering
[2] **decanted:** poured from one container to another
[3] **susurration:** murmur; whisper

A CLOSER LOOK

1. In what ways is life in space — as described in this story — different from life on Earth? In what ways is life in space similar to life on Earth? What sorts of people do you think would be attracted to this life in space?

2. At the beginning of the story, how does the narrator seem to feel about life in space? How do his feelings change?

3. Imagine yourself in the space suit, hearing the same strange sounds. Would you react in the same way as the narrator? Why or why not? Were you pleased with the ending of the story? Were you disappointed with the ending? Why?

● If you could send a message of advice to people on other planets, what would you say? Would you tell them to build more powerful weapons? Or would you tell them — as Olga Cabral does — that no weapon is mightier than love?

Olga Cabral

ELECTRONIC TAPE FOUND IN A BOTTLE

If this small human testament[1]
completes its odyssey[2]
clears the curtains of fiery meteors
crosses the rages of magnetic storms
rides free of hydrogen whirlwinds
falls through coalsack eternities
lands smoothly on the Milky Way
glides along its lightband
to the shores of an unknown planet
in an unknown star-continent
to be found and wonderingly
pondered[3] held in your hands —
this message was meant for you.

Be advised that I live on
a small green ball in the suburbs
of an unremarkable sun

that had begun to run down.
Our race was a sun-people
but died of diseases called wars.
To you out there in star cities
with your libraries, fountains
or you who are still making it
through ice ages of ignorance —
whoever or whatever you are
here is earth's final message:
I love you I love you I love you.

There is nothing more to say
there was nothing better here
and nothing in all the spiraling nebulae[4]
was as frail or as mighty as this.

[1] **testament:** a statement of belief
[2] **odyssey:** a long voyage
[3] **pondered:** considered; thought about
[4] **nebulae:** galaxies

"Get out while you can."

Allan Danzig

THE GREAT NEBRASKA SEA

● When bad things happen to us, it seems as though the world is coming to an end. But in time we can step back and see things in a different light. Imagine that you are reading a magazine in the year 2090. A writer is explaining a natural event that happened almost a century ago. It's easy to describe such things in calm, objective language when they happened in the past. But that writer's past is still in our future!

EVERYONE — ALL THE GEOLOGISTS,[1] AT ANY rate — had known about the Kiowa Fault[2] for years. This was before there was anything very interesting to know about it. The first survey of Colorado traced its course north and south in the narrow valley of Kiowa Creek about twenty miles east of Denver; it extended south to the Arkansas River. And that was about all even the professionals were interested in knowing. There was never so much as a landslide to bring the Fault to the attention of the general public.

It was still a matter of academic[3] interest when in the late 1940's geologists studied the relationship between the Kiowa Fault and the Conchas Fault farther south, in New Mexico.

Nor was there much in the papers a few years later when it was suggested that the Niobrara Fault (just inside the eastern border of Wyoming) was a northerly extension of the Kiowa. By the mid-sixties it was definitely established that the three faults were in fact a single line of fissure[4] in the essential rock, stretching almost from the Canadian border well south of the New Mexico-Texas line.

It is not really surprising that it took so long to figure out the connection. The population of the states affected was in places as low as five people per square mile! The land was so dry it seemed impossible that it would ever be used except for sheep farming.

The solution to the problem began in the summer of 1993. It had been a particularly hot and dry August, and the Forestry Service was keeping an anxious eye out for the fires it knew it could expect. Dense smoke was reported above a virtually uninhabited area along Black Squirrel Creek, and a plane was sent out for a report.

The report was — no fire at all. The rising cloud was not smoke, but dust — thousands of cubic feet of dry earth rising lazily on the summer air. Rock slides, they guessed; certainly no fire. The Forestry Service had other worries at the moment, and filed the report.

But after a week had gone by, the town of Edison, a good twenty miles away from the slides, was still complaining of the dust. Springs were going dry, too, apparently from underground disturbances. Not even in the Rockies could anyone remember a series of rock slides as bad as this.

Newspapers in the Mountain states gave it a few inches on the front page; anything is news in late August. And the geologists became interested. Seismologists[5] were reporting unusual activity in the area, tremors too severe to be rock slides. Volcanic activity? Specifically, a dust volcano? Unusual, they knew, but right on the Kiowa Fault — could be.

It may seem odd that the simplest explanation was practically not mentioned. Only Joseph Schwartzberg, head geographer of the Department of the Interior, wondered if the disturbance might not be a settling[6] of the Kiowa Fault. His suggestion was mentioned on page nine or ten of the Monday newspapers (page 27 of *The New York Times*). The idea was clearly not as exciting as a volcano, even a lavaless one, and you couldn't draw a very dramatic picture of it.

To excuse the other geologists, it must be said that the Kiowa Fault had never acted up before. It never side-stepped, never jiggled, never, never produced the regular shows of its little sister out in California, which almost daily bounced San Francisco or Los Angeles, or some place in between. The dust volcano was on the face of it a more believable theory.

Still, it was only a theory. It had to be proved. As the tremors grew bigger, along with the affected area, and as several towns including Edison were shaken to pieces by incredible earthquakes, whole bus- and plane-loads of geologists set out for Colorado, without even waiting for their university and government departments to approve budgets.

They found, of course, that Schwartzberg had been perfectly correct.

They found themselves on the scene of what was fast becoming the most violent and widespread earthquake North America — probably the world — has ever seen in historic times. To describe it in the simplest terms, land east of the Fault was settling, and at a rapid rate.

Rock scraped rock with a whining roar. The surfaces of the land east and west of the Fault seemed no longer to have any relation to each other. To the west, tortured rocks reared into cliffs. To the east, the earth trembled downward. The new cliffs seemed to grow by sudden inches from heaving rubble. Dry earth fissured and trembled, sliding acres at a time to fall, smoking, into the bucking, heaving bottom of the depression.[7]

There the destruction was even more thorough, if less spectacular. Dry earth churned like mud. Rocks weighing tons bumped and rolled about like pebbles as they shivered and cracked into pebbles themselves. "It looks like sand dancing in a child's sieve,"[8] said the normally quiet Schwartzberg in a nationwide broadcast from the scene of the disaster. "No one here has ever seen anything like it." And the landslip was growing, north and south along the Fault.

"Get out while you can," Schwartzberg urged the population of the affected area. "When it's over you can come back and pick up the pieces." But the band of scientists who had rallied to his leadership privately wondered if there would be any pieces.

The Arkansas River, at Avondale and North Avondale, was slowly backing north into the deepening trough. At the rate things were going, there might be a new lake the entire length of El Paso and Pueblo counties. And, warned Schwartzberg, this might only be the beginning.

By September 16th the landslip had crept down the Huerfano River past Cedarwood. Avondale, North Avondale, and Boone had totally disappeared. Land west of the Fault was holding firm, though Denver had recorded several small tremors. Everywhere east of the Fault, to almost twenty miles away, the now-familiar lurch and steady fall had already sent several thousand people scurrying for safety.

"Soon the Missouri began slipping away westward."

All mountain climbing was forbidden on the eastern slope because of the danger of rock slides from minor quakes. The geologists went home to wait.

There wasn't much to wait for. The news got worse and worse. The Platte River, now, was creating a vast puddle where the town of Orchard had been. Just below Masters, Colorado, the river had leaped seventy-foot cliffs to add to the chaos below. And the cliffs were higher every day as the land beneath them groaned downward in mile-square gulps.

As the Fault moved north and south, new areas quivered into unwelcome life. Telephone lines, railroad tracks, roads snapped and simply disappeared. Virtually all east-west land communication was suspended, and the President declared a national emergency.

By September 23rd the Fault was active well into Wyoming on the north, and rapidly approaching the border of New Mexico to the south. Trinchera and Branson were totally evacuated, but even so, the overall death toll had risen above one thousand.

Away to the east the situation was quiet but even more threatening. Tremendous fissures opened up perpendicular to the Fault. The western borders of Kansas and Nebraska, and soon of the Dakotas and Oklahoma as well, were slowly sinking.

On the actual scene of the disaster (or the *scenes*: it is impossible to speak of anything this size in the singular) there was a horrifying confusion. Prairie and hill cracked open under unbearable strains as the land shuddered downward in gasps and leaps. Springs burst to the surface in hot geysers and explosions of steam.

The downtown section of North Platte, Nebraska, dropped eight feet, just like that, on the afternoon of October 4th. "We must remain calm," declared the Governor of Nebraska. "We must sit this thing out. Be assured that everything possible is being done." But what could be done, with his state dropping straight down at a mean rate of a foot a day?

The Fault nicked off the southeast corner of Montana. It worked its way north along the Little Missouri. South, it ripped past Roswell, New Mexico, and tore down the Pecos toward Texas. All the upper reaches of the Missouri were standing puddles by now, and the Red River west of Paris, Texas, had begun to run backward.

Soon the Missouri began slipping away westward over the slowly churning land. Abandoning its bed, the river spread uncertainly across farmland and prairie, becoming a sea of mud beneath the sharp new cliffs. There were virtually no floods, in the usual sense. The water moved too slowly, spread itself with no real direction or force. But the vast sheets of sluggish water and jellylike mud formed deathtraps for the countless refugees now streaming east.

By October 7th it had to be officially admitted that there was an exodus[9] of epic proportion. Nearly two million people were on the move, and the U.S. was faced with a gigantic wave of refugees. Rails, roads, and airlanes were jammed with terrified hordes who had left everything behind to crowd eastward.

On October 21st, at Lubbock, Texas, there was a noise variously described as a hollow roar, a shriek, and a deep musical vibration like a church bell. It was simply the tortured rock of the substrata[10] giving way. The second phase of the national disaster was beginning.

The noise traveled due east at better than eighty-five miles per hour. In its wake the earth to the north "just seemed to collapse on itself like a punctured balloon," read one newspaper report. "Like a cake that's failed," said a Texarkana housewife who fortunately lived a block *south* of Thayer Street, where the fissure raced through. There was a sigh and a great cloud of dust, and Oklahoma

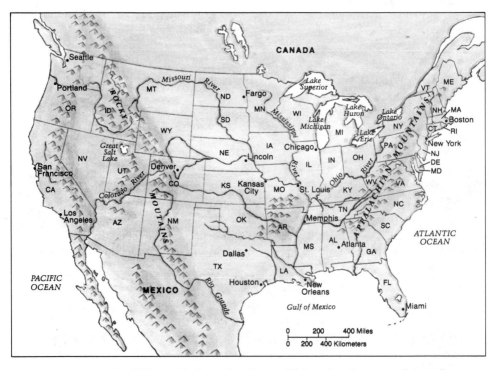

The United States before the Great Nebraska Sea was formed.

sank at the astounding rate of six feet per hour.

At Biloxi, on the Gulf, there had been uneasy shufflings under foot all day. "Not tremors, exactly," said the captain of a fishing boat which was somehow to ride out of the coming flood, "but like as if the land wanted to be somewhere else."

Everyone in doomed Biloxi would have done well to have been somewhere else that evening. At approximately 8:30 p.m. the town shuddered, seemed to rise a little like the edge of a hall carpet caught in a draft, and sank. So did the entire Mississippi and Alabama coast, at about the same moment. The tidal wave which was to gouge the center from the U.S. marched on land.

From the north shore of Lake Ponchartrain to the Appalachicola River in Florida, the Gulf coast simply disappeared. Two hundred miles of shoreline vanished, with over two and a half million people. An hour later a wall of water had swept over every town from Dothan, Alabama, to Bogalusa on the Louisiana-Mississippi border.

"We must keep panic from our minds," said the Governor of Alabama in a radio message delivered from a hastily arranged all-station hookup. "We of the gallant southland have faced and withstood invasion before." Then, as creakings and groanings of the

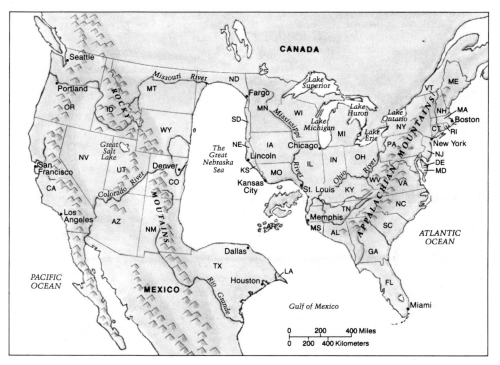

The United States today.

earth announced the approach of the tidal wave, he flew out of Montgomery half an hour before the town disappeared forever.

The Mississippi River now ended at about Eudora, Arkansas, and minute by minute the advancing flood bit away miles of riverbed, swelling north. Chicot, Jennie, Lake Village, Arkansas City, Snow Lake, Elaine, Helena, and Memphis felt the tremors. The tormented city shuddered through the night. The earth continued its descent, eventually tipping 2.5 degrees down to the west. The "Memphis Tilt" is today one of the unique and charming characteristics of the gracious Old Town, but during the night of panic Memphis residents were sure they were doomed.

South and west the waters carved deeply into Arkansas and Oklahoma. By morning it was plain that all of Arkansas was going under. Waves advanced on Little Rock at almost one hundred miles an hour.

Washington announced the official hope that the Ozark Mountains would stop the wild gallop of the unleashed Gulf, for in northwest Arkansas the land rose to over two thousand feet. But nothing could save Oklahoma. By noon the water reached clutching fingers around Mt. Scott, deluging almost all of Greer County.

"The barn luckily collapsed as the waves bore down on them."

The wall of water continued its advance. For the land was still sinking, and the floods were constantly replenished[11] from the Gulf.

Lubbock, Texas, went under. The Texas panhandle disappeared in one great swirl.

Whirlpools opened. Gulf water crashed on the cliffs of New Mexico and fell back on itself in foam. Would-be rescuers on the cliffs along what had been the west bank of the Pecos River afterward recalled the hiss and scream like tearing silk as the water broke furiously on the newly exposed rock. It was the most horrible sound they had ever heard.

"We couldn't hear any shouts, of course, not that far away and with all the noise," said Dan Weaver, Mayor of Carlsbad. "But we knew there were people down there. When the water hit the cliffs, it was like a collision between two solid bodies. We couldn't see for over an hour, because of the spray."

Salt spray: The ocean had come to New Mexico.

The cliffs proved to be the only effective barrier against the westward march of the water, which turned north, gouging out lumps of rock and tumbling down blocks of earth onto its own back. In places scoops of granite came out like ice cream. The present fishing town of Rockport, Colorado, is built on a harbor created in such a way.

The water had found its farthest westering. But still it poured north along the line of the original Fault.

Memphis was by now a seaport. Waves bit off a corner of Missouri, flung themselves on Wichita. Topeka, Lawrence, and Belleville were the last Kansas towns to disappear. The Governor of Kansas went down with his state.

Daniel Bernd of Lincoln, Nebraska, was washed up half-drowned in a cove of the Wyoming cliffs. He had been sucked from one end of vanished Nebraska to the other. Similar hairbreadth escapes were recounted on radio and television.

Virtually the only people saved out of the entire population of Pierre, South Dakota, were the six members of the Creeth family. Plucky Timothy Creeth carried and dragged his aged parents to the loft of their barn on the outskirts of town. His brother Geoffrey brought along the younger children and what provisions they could find — "Mostly a ham and about half a ton of vanilla cookies," he explained to his eventual rescuers. The barn luckily collapsed as the waves bore down on them, and became an ark in which they rode out the disaster.

"We must have played cards for four days straight," recalled Mrs. Creeth when she afterward appeared on a popular television spectacular. Her rural good humor was undamaged by an ordeal few women can ever have been called on to face. "We sure wondered why flushes never came out right," she added. "We'd left the king of hearts behind, in the rush!"

But such lightheartedness and such happy ending were by no means typical. The world could only watch in horror as the water raced north under the shadow of the cliffs which occasionally crumbled, roaring, into the roaring waves. Day by day the rushing waters swallowed what had been dusty farmland, cities, and towns.

Some people were saved by the helicopters which flew mercy missions just ahead of the advancing waters. Some found safety in the peaks of western Nebraska and the Dakotas. But when the waters came to rest along what is roughly the present shoreline of our inland sea, it was estimated that over fourteen million people had lost their lives.

No one could even estimate the damage to property: almost all of eight states and portions of twelve others had simply vanished.

It was in such a cataclysmic[12] birth that the now-peaceful Nebraska Sea came to America.

Today, nearly one hundred years after the disaster, it is hard to remember the terror and despair of those weeks in October and November. It is inconceivable to think of the United States without its beautifully and economically essential curve of interior ocean. It is two-thirds as long as the Mediterranean and graduates[13] from the warm waters of the Gulf of Mexico through the equally blue waves of the Mississippi Bight. It becomes cooler and greener north and west of the pleasant fishing isles of the Ozark Archipelago, and finally shades into the gray-green chop of the Gulf of Dakota.

What would the United States have become without the 5,600-mile coastline of our inland sea? It is only within the last twenty years that the water has cleared sufficiently to permit a really large fishing industry. Even so, the commercial fisheries of Missouri and Wyoming contribute no small part to the nation's economy.

Who can imagine what the Middle West must have been like before the improved climate brought about by the nearness of a

"It is hard to remember the terror and despair of those weeks."

warm sea? The now-warm state of Minnesota (to say nothing of the submerged Dakotas) must have been as cold as Siberia.

Who today could imagine the United States without the majestic sea cliffs from New Mexico to Montana? Or the beaches of Wyoming, the American Riviera, where fruit trees grow almost to the water's edge? Or incredible Colorado, where the morning skier is the afternoon bather, thanks to the monorail connecting the highest peaks with the glistening white beaches?

Of course there have been losses to balance slightly these strong gains. The Mississippi was, before 1993, one of three great rivers of the world. Taken together with its main tributary, the Missouri, it vied favorably with such giant systems as the Amazon and the Ganges. Now, ending as it does at Memphis and drawing its water chiefly from the Appalachian Mountains, it is only a slight remnant[14] of what it was. And though the Nebraska Sea today carries many times the tonnage of shipping in its ceaseless traffic, we have lost the old romance of river shipping.

Transcontinental shipping is somewhat more difficult, with trucks and the freight-railroads obliged to take the sea ferries across the Nebraska Sea. We shall never know what the United States was like with its numerous coast-to-coast highways busy with trucks and private cars. Still, the ferry ride is certainly a welcome break after days of driving, and for those who wish a glimpse of what it must have been like, there is always the Cross-Canada Throughway and the magnificent U.S. Highway 73 looping north through Minnesota and passing through the giant port of Alexis, North Dakota, shipping center for the wheat of Manitoba and crossroad of a nation.

The political situation has long been a thorny problem. Only tattered remnants of the eight submerged states remained after the flood, but none of them wanted to surrender its independence. The tiny fringe of Kansas seemed, for a time, ready to merge with Missouri. But following the lead of the Arkansas Forever faction, the remaining population decided to keep its political independence. This has resulted in the seven "fringe states" represented in Congress by the usual two senators each, though the largest of them is barely the size of Connecticut and all are economically indistinguishable from their neighboring states.

Fortunately, it was decided some years ago that Oklahoma, the only one of the eight to have completely disappeared, could not in any sense be considered to have a continuing political existence. So, though there are still families who proudly call themselves Oklahomans, and the Oklahoma Oil Company continues to pump oil from its submerged real estate, the state has in fact disappeared from the American political scene.

But this is by now no more than a petty annoyance, which raises a smile when the talk gets around to the question of states' rights. Not even the tremendous price the country paid for its new sea — fourteen million dead, untold property destroyed — really offsets the asset we enjoy today. The heart of the continent, now open to the shipping of the world, was once dry and landlocked, cut off from the bustle of trade and world culture.

It would indeed seem odd to an American of the last century to imagine sailors from the merchant fleets of every nation walking the streets of Denver. Or to imagine Lincoln, Fargo, Kansas City, and Dallas as world ports and great manufacturing centers. Utterly beyond their understanding would be Roswell, New Mexico; Benton, Wyoming; Westport, Missouri, and the other new ports of over a million inhabitants each which have developed on the new harbors of the inland sea.

Unimaginable too would have been the general growth of population in the states surrounding the new sea. As the water tables rose and manufacturing and trade moved in, a population explosion was touched off of which we are only now seeing the end. This new westering is to be ranked with the first surge of pioneers which created the American west. But what a difference! Vacation paradises bloom, a new fishing industry thrives; her water road is America's main artery of trade, and fleets of all the world sail . . . where once the covered wagon made its laborious[15] and dusty way west!

[1] **geologists:** people who study the history of the earth, especially as recorded in rocks
[2] **fault:** a crack or fracture in the Earth's crust
[3] **academic:** of no practical or useful importance
[4] **fissure:** a narrow opening or crack
[5] **seismologists:** scientists who specialize in earthquakes and vibrations of the Earth
[6] **settling:** becoming compact by sinking
[7] **depression:** hole; cavity
[8] **sieve:** a device with meshes or small holes through which fine particles can pass
[9] **exodus:** a mass departure
[10] **substrata:** foundation; the layer beneath the surface
[11] **replenished:** filled up again
[12] **cataclysmic:** disastrous; marked by violent geological change
[13] **graduates:** gradually changes
[14] **remnant:** a small remaining part
[15] **laborious:** hard; full of toil

A CLOSER LOOK

1. How do the people in charge — the geologists and the elected officials — react to this disaster? What attitudes do they share? Why do you think they act the way they do?

2. How does the writer seem to feel about the events he is discussing? Is he horrified, or amused? Is he involved, or uninvolved? Do you think he would have written a different type of essay five years after the earthquake? Why or why not?

3. What are the long-term effects of this earthquake? How does the magazine writer seem to feel about these effects? How do you feel about them?

"Well, the thing is, I can't remember."

W. Hilton-Young

THE CHOICE

● The children in Ray Bradbury's story (page 44) travel into the past; here's a story about a time traveller from our own age who heads into the future. The choice in this story is not his — it's yours!

EFORE WILLIAMS WENT INTO THE FUTURE, HE
bought a camera and a tape recording machine and learned
shorthand. That night, when all was ready, we made coffee
for his return.

"Good-bye," I said. "Don't stay too long."

"I won't," he answered.

I watched him carefully, and he hardly flickered.

Williams must have made a perfect landing on the very second he
had taken off. He seemed not a day older; we had expected he might
spend several years away.

"Well?"

"Well," said he, "let's have some coffee."

I poured it out, hardly able to contain my impatience. As I gave it
to him, I said again, "Well?"

"Well, the thing is, I can't remember."

"Can't remember? Not a thing?"

He thought for a moment and answered sadly, "Not a thing."

147

"But your notes? The camera? The recording machine?"

The notebook was empty, and the indicator of the camera rested at "1" where we had set it. The tape was not even loaded into the recording machine.

"But good heavens," I protested, "why?" How did it happen? Can you remember nothing at all?"

"I can remember only one thing."

"What was that?"

"I was shown everything, and I was given the choice whether I should remember it or not after I got back."

"And you chose not to? But what an extraordinary thing to — "

"Isn't it?" he said. "One can't help wondering why."

A CLOSER LOOK

1. How long was Williams gone from the room? How long do you think he stayed in the future?

2. Why do you think Williams decided to forget what he saw?

3. What do you think you would see if you travelled a hundred years into the future? Would you want to remember what you saw?

Frederic Brown

PREPOSTEROUS

● People laugh at new ideas — until they come true. There will always be people like Mr. Weatherwax, who are afraid of change; and there will always be imaginative children like Gerald, who keep the world from standing still.

MR. WEATHERWAX BUTTERED HIS TOAST CARE-fully. His voice was firm. "My dear," he said, "I want it definitely understood that there shall be no more trashy reading around this apartment."

"Yes, Jason. I did not know — "

"Of course you didn't. But it is your responsibility to know what our son reads."

"I shall watch him more closely, Jason. I did not see the magazine when he brought it in. I did not know it was here."

"Nor would I have known had I not, after I came in last night, accidentally happened to displace one of the pillows on the sofa. The periodical was hidden under it, and of course I glanced through it."

The points of Mr. Weatherwax's mustache quivered in indignation. "Such utterly ridiculous concepts, such impossibly wild ideas. *Astounding Stories,* indeed!"

He took a sip of coffee to calm himself.

"Such insane and utterly preposterous nonsense," he said. "Travel to other galaxies by means of space warps, whatever they are. Time machines, teleportation, and telekinesis. Nonsense, sheer nonsense."

"Such impossibly wild ideas."

"My dear Jason," said his wife, this time with just the faintest touch of asperity.[1] "I assure you I shall watch Gerald's reading closely hereafter. I fully agree with you."

"Thank you, my dear," Mr. Weatherwax said, more kindly. "The minds of the young should not be poisoned by such wild imaginings."

He glanced at his watch and rose hastily, kissed his wife, and left.

Outside the apartment door he stepped into the antigravity shaft and floated gently down two hundred-odd floors to street level where he was lucky enough to catch an atomcab inmmediately. "Moon-port," he snapped at the robot driver, and then sat back and closed his eyes to catch the telepathecast. He'd hoped to catch a bulletin on the Fourth Martian War, but it was only another report from Cyborg Center, so he quirtled.[2]

[1] **asperity:** bitterness
[2] **quirtled:** a science fiction word based apparently on the verb "quirt," meaning to strike or drive with a riding whip

A CLOSER LOOK

1. Why do you think Mr. Weatherwax is so upset? Why do you think the author chose the name Weatherwax for this character?

2. Does the story take place in the present or in the future? Why does the author withhold this information until you've read most of the story?

3. Why do you think Gerald reads science fiction? If you were his parent, would you stop him from reading science fiction? Or would you encourage him to read science fiction? Explain your answer.

• The Earth is only a tiny part of this great cosmos. Yet we all live at the center of a world of our own.

Edward Field

PROLOGUE[1]

Look, friend, at this universe
with its spiral clusters of stars
flying out all over space
like bedsprings suddenly busting free,
and in this galaxy, the sun,
fissioning[2] itself away,
surrounded by planets, prominent[3] in their dignity,
and bits and pieces running wild,
and this middling[4] planet
with a lone[5] moon circling round it.

Look, friend, through the fog of gases at this world
with its skin of earth and rock, water and ice,

with various creatures and rooted things,
and up from the bulging waistline
to this land of concrete towers,
its roads swarming like a hive cut open,
offshore to this island, long and fishshaped,
its mouth to a metropolis,[6]
and in its belly, this village,
a gathering of families at a crossways,
and in this house, upstairs and through the wide open door
of the front bedroom with a window on the world,
look, friend, at me.

[1] **prologue:** an introductory speech or event
[2] **fissioning:** breaking into parts
[3] **prominent:** standing out; noticeable
[4] **middling:** of medium size
[5] **lone:** single; alone
[6] **metropolis:** a large city

"I have saved what I loved."

154

Walter Van Tilburg Clark

THE PORTABLE PHONOGRAPH

● In the wasteland left by total war, four human survivors lead a primitive life. All, however, carry within them a memory of the civilization that once was. They treasure the scraps of art and culture they have preserved — but is this enough to make them civilized?

THE RED SUNSET, WITH NARROW, BLACK CLOUD strips like threats across it, lay on the curved horizon of the prairie. The air was still and cold, and in it settled the mute[1] darkness and greater cold of night. High in the air there was wind. Through the veil of the dusk, the clouds could be seen gliding rapidly south and changing shapes. A queer sensation of torment, of two-sided, unpredictable nature, arose from the stillness of the earth air beneath the violence of the upper air. Out of the sunset, through the dead, matted grass and isolated weed stalks of the prairie, crept the narrow and deeply rutted remains of a road. In the road, in places, there were crusts of shallow, brittle ice. There were little islands of an old oiled pavement in the road, too, but most of it was mud, now frozen rigid. The frozen mud still bore the toothed impress of great tanks. A wanderer on the neighboring undulations[2] might have stumbled in this light, into large, partially filled-in and weedgrown cavities, their banks channeled and beginning to spread into badlands.[3] These pits were such as might have been made by falling meteors, but they were not. They were the scars of gigantic

155

bombs, their rawness already made a little natural by rain, seed, and time.

Along the road there were rakish remnants of fence. There was also, just visible, one portion of tangled and multiple barbed wire still erect, behind which was a shelving ditch with small caves, now very quiet and empty, at intervals in its back wall. Otherwise, there was no structure or remnant of a structure visible over the dome of the darkling earth, but only, in sheltered hollows, the darker shadows of young trees trying again.

Under the wuthering[4] arch of the high wind, a V of wild geese fled south. The rush of their pinions[5] sounded briefly, and the faint, plaintive[6] notes of their expeditionary talk. Then they left a still greater vacancy. There was the smell and expectation of snow, as there is likely to be when the wild geese fly south. From the remote distance, toward the red sky, came faintly the protracted[7] howl and quick yap-yap of a prairie wolf.

North of the road, perhaps a hundred yards, lay the parallel and deeply intrenched course of a small creek, lined with leafless alders and willows. The creek was already silent under ice. Into the bank above it was dug a sort of cell, with a single opening like the mouth of a mine tunnel. Within the cell there was a little red of fire, which showed dully through the opening, like a reflection or a deception of the imagination. The light came from the chary[8] burning of four blocks of poorly aged peat,[9] which gave off a petty warmth and much acrid[10] smoke. But the precious remnants of wood, old fence posts,and timbers from the long-deserted dugouts had to be saved for the real cold, for the time when a man's breath blew white, the moisture in his nostrils stiffened at once when he stepped out, and the expansive blizzards paraded for days over the vast open, swirling and settling and thickening till the dawn of the cleared day when the sky was a thin blue-green and the terrible cold, in which a man could not live for three hours unwarmed, lay over the uniformly drifted swell of the plain.

Around the smoldering peat four men were seated crosslegged. Behind them, traversed[11] by their shadows, was the earth bench, with two old and dirty Army blankets, where the owner of the cell slept. In a niche in the opposite wall were a few tin utensils which caught the glint of the coals. The host was rewrapping in a piece of daubed burlap four fine, leather-bound books. He worked slowly and very carefully and at last tied the bundle securely with a piece of grass-woven cord. The other three looked intently upon the process, as if a great significance lay in it. As the host tied the cord, he spoke. He was an old man, his long, matted beard and hair gray to nearly white. The shadows made his brows and cheekbones appear gnarled, his eyes and cheeks deeply sunken. His big hands, rough with frost and swollen by rheumatism, were awkward but gentle at their task. He was like a prehistoric priest performing a fateful ceremonial rite. Also, his voice had in it a suitable quality of deep, reverent despair, yet perhaps at the moment, a sharpness of selfish satisfaction. "When I perceived what was happening," he said, "I told myself, 'It is the end, I cannot take much; I will take these.'

"Perhaps I was impractical," he continued. "But for myself, I do not regret, and what do we know of those who will come after us? We are the doddering[12] remnant of a race of mechanical fools. I have saved what I love; the soul of what was good in us is here; perhaps the new ones will make a strong enough beginning not to fall behind when they become clever."

He rose with slow pain and placed the wrapped volumes in the niche with his utensils. The others watched him with the same ritualistic gaze.

"Shakespeare, the Bible, *Moby Dick,* the *Divine Comedy,*" one of them said softly. "You might have done worse, much worse."

"You will have a little soul left until you die," said another harshly. "That is more than is true of us. My brain becomes thick, like my hands." He held the big, battered hands, with their black nails, in the glow to be seen.

"I want paper to write on," he said. "And there is none."

The fourth man said nothing. He sat in the shadow farthest from the fire, and sometimes his body jerked in its rags from the cold. Although he was still young, he was sick and coughed often. Writing implied a greater future than he now felt able to consider.

The old man seated himself laboriously, and reached out, groaning at the movement, to put another block of peat on the fire. With bowed heads and averted eyes, his three guests acknowledged his magnanimity.[13]

"We thank you, Doctor Jenkins, for the reading," said the man who had named the books.

They seemed then to be waiting for something. Doctor Jenkins understood, but was loath to comply. In an ordinary moment he would have said nothing. But the words of *The Tempest,*[14] which he had been reading, and the religious attention of the three, made this an unusual occasion.

"You wish to hear the phonograph," he said grudgingly.

The two middle-aged men stared into the fire, unable to formulate and expose the enormity of their desire.

The young man, however, said anxiously, between suppressed coughs, "Oh, please," like an excited child.

The old man rose again in his difficult way, and went to the back of the cell. He returned and placed tenderly upon the packed floor, where the firelight might fall upon it, an old portable phonograph in a black case. He smoothed the top with his hand, and then opened it. The lovely green felt-covered disc became visible.

"I have been using thorns as needles," he said. "But tonight, because we have a musician among us" — he bent his head to the young man, almost invisible in the shadow — "I will use a steel needle. There are only three left."

The two middle-aged men stared at him in speechless adoration. The one with the big hands, who wanted to write, moved his lips, but the whisper was not audible.

"Oh, don't!" cried the young man, as if he were hurt. "The thorns will do beautifully."

"No," the old man said. "I have become accustomed to the thorns, but they are not really good. For you, my young friend, we will have good music tonight.

"After all," he added generously, and beginning to wind the phonograph, which creaked, "They can't last forever."

"No, nor we," the man who needed to write said harshly. "The needle, by all means."

"Oh, thanks," said the young man. "Thanks," he said again in a low, excited voice, and then stifled his coughing with a bowed head.

"The records, though," said the old man when he had finished winding, "are a different matter. Already they are very worn. I do not play them more than once a week. One, once a week, that is what I allow myself.

"More than a week I cannot stand it; not to hear them," he apologized.

"No, how could you?" cried the young man. "And with them here like this."

"A man can stand anything," said the man who wanted to write, in his harsh, antagonistic voice.

"I do not play them more than once a week."

"Please, the music," said the young man.

"Only the one," said the old man. "In the long run, we will remember more that way."

He had a dozen records with luxuriant gold and red seals. Even in that light the others could see that the threads of the records were becoming worn. Slowly he read out the titles, and the tremendous, dead names of the composers and the artists and the orchestras. The three worked upon the names in their minds, carefully. It was difficult to select from such a wealth what they would at once most like to remember. Finally, the man who wanted to write named Gershwin's "New York."

"Oh, no!" cried the sick young man, and then could say nothing more because he had to cough. The others understood him, and the harsh man withdrew his selection and waited for the musician to choose.

The musician begged Doctor Jenkins to read the titles again, very slowly, so that he could remember the sounds. While they were read, he lay back against the wall, his eyes closed, his thin, horny hand pulling at his light beard, and listened to the voices and the orchestras and the single instruments in his mind.

When the reading was done, he spoke despairingly. "I have forgotten," he complained; "I cannot hear them clearly."

"There are things missing," he explained.

"I know," said Doctor Jenkins. "I thought that I knew all of Shelley[15] by heart. I should have brought Shelley."

"That's more soul than we can use," said the harsh man. "*Moby Dick* is better.

"We can understand that," he emphasized.

The doctor nodded.

"Still," said the man who had admired the books, "we need the absolute if we are to keep a grasp on anything."

"Anything but these sticks and peat clods and rabbit snares," he said bitterly.

"Shelley desired an ultimate absolute," said the harsh man. "It's too much," he said. "It's no good; no earthly good."

The musician selected a Debussy nocturne.[16] The others considered and approved. They rose to their knees to watch the doctor prepare for the playing, so that they appeared to be actually in an attitude of worship. The peat glow showed the thinness of their bearded faces, and the deep lines in them, and revealed the condition of their garments. The other two continued to kneel as the old man carefully lowered the needle onto the spinning disc, but the musician suddenly drew back against the wall again, with his knees up, and buried his face in his hands.

At the first notes of the piano, the listeners were startled. They stared at each other. Even the musician lifted his head in amazement, but then quickly bowed it again, strainingly, as if he were suffering from a pain he might not be able to endure. They were all listening deeply, without movement. The wet, blue-green notes tinkled forth from the old machine, and were individual, delectable[17] presences in the cell. The individual, delectable presences swept into a sudden tide of unbearably beautiful dissonance,[18] and then continued fully the swelling and ebbing of that tide, the dissonant inpourings and the resolutions and the diminishments[19] and the little, quiet wavelets of interlude[20] lapping between. Every sound was piercing and singularly sweet. In all the men except the musician there occurred rapid sequences of tragically heightened recollection. He heard nothing but what was there. At the final, whispering disappearance, but moving quietly so that the others would not hear him and look at him, he let his head fall back in agony, as if it were drawn there by the hair, and clenched the fingers of one hand over his teeth. He sat that way while the others were silent, and until they began to breathe again normally. His drawn-up legs were trembling violently.

Quickly Doctor Jenkins lifted the needle off, to save it and not spoil the recollection with scraping. When he had stopped the whirling of the sacred disc, he courteously left the phonograph open and by the fire, in sight.

The others, however, understood. The musician rose last, but then abruptly, and went quickly out at the door without saying anything. The others stopped at the door and gave their thanks in low voices. The doctor nodded magnificently.

"Come again," he invited, "in a week. We will have the 'New York.' "

When the two had gone together, out toward the rimed[21] road, he stood in the entrance, peering and listening. At first, there was only the resonant boom of the wind overhead, and then far over the dome of the dead, dark plain, the wolf cry lamenting. In the rifts of clouds, the doctor saw four stars flying. It impressed the doctor that one of them had just been obscured by the beginning of a flying cloud at the very moment he heard what he had been listening for, a sound of suppressed coughing. It was not nearby, however. He believed that down against the pale alders he could see the moving shadow.

With nervous hands he lowered the piece of canvas which served as his door, and pegged it at the bottom. Then quickly and quietly, looking at the piece of canvas frequently, he slipped the records into the case, snapped the lid shut, and carried the phonograph to his couch. There, pausing to stare at the canvas and listen, he dug earth from the wall and disclosed a piece of board. Behind this there was a deep hole in the wall into which he put the phonograph. After a moment's consideration, he went over and reached down his bundle of books and inserted it also. Then, guardedly, he once more sealed up the hole with the board and the earth. He also changed his blankets, and the grass-stuffed sack which served as a pillow, so that he could lie facing the entrance. After carefully placing two more blocks of peat upon the fire, he stood for a long time watching the stretched canvas, but it seemed to billow naturally with the first gusts of a lowering wind. At last he prayed and got in under his blankets and closed his smoke-smarting eyes. On the inside of the bed, next to the wall, he could feel with his hand the comfortable piece of lead pipe.

[1] **mute:** silent; felt but not put into words
[2] **undulations:** wave-like forms
[3] **badlands:** a region with little vegetation and weirdly shaped hills
[4] **wuthering:** blowing with a dull, roaring sound
[5] **pinions:** wings
[6] **plaintive:** mournful; sad
[7] **protracted:** drawn out
[8] **chary:** slow; cautious
[9] **peat:** turf formed by the decay of plants in water, sometimes used for heating in place of wood
[10] **acrid:** sharp; unpleasant
[11] **traversed:** crossed
[12] **doddering:** shaking from weakness or age
[13] **magnanimity:** lofty spirits; a quality that makes a person bear troubles
[14] ***The Tempest:*** a play by Shakespeare
[15] **Shelley, Percy Bysshe** (1792-1822): an English Romantic poet who created, in verse, a world of pure imagination
[16] **Debussy, Claude** (1862-1918): a French composer; his **nocturnes** were dreamy compositions that captured the mood of evening
[17] **delectable:** highly pleasing
[18] **dissonance:** discord; harsh or clashing sound
[19] **diminishments:** decreases in size or importance
[20] **interlude:** interval; light musical composition between the two parts of a longer work
[21] **rimed:** covered with granular ice, formed by cooled fog and wind

A CLOSER LOOK

1. In what ways are the four survivors different? In what ways are they the same? What does each man value most? Why? What does each fear most?

2. What do you think would happen to these men without their books and music? Does society need art — music, dance, literature, and so on — in order to survive? Why or why not?

3. Imagine you could preserve only a few of the things you use and enjoy today. If you could only preserve four books, which ones would you choose? Name four other possessions you would keep.

Carl Sagan

THE HUMAN FAMILY

● Astronomer Carl Sagan has spent a lifetime thinking about the cosmos. In this brief essay from Cosmos — the best selling science book ever published in the English language — he asks you to think about your place, as Earthlings, in our vast universe.

W E HAVE BELIEVED THAT A PERSON OR SOCIETY that is a little different from us is somehow strange, and to be distrusted or hated. And yet the monuments and cultures of each of our civilizations merely represent different ways of being human.

An extraterrestial visitor, looking at the differences among human beings and their societies, would find those differences trivial compared to the similarities. The cosmos may be populated with intelligent beings, but there will be no humans elsewhere. Only here. Only on this small planet. We are a rare as well as an endangered species. Every one of us is, in relation to the cosmos, unique. If a human disagrees with you, let him live. In a hundred billion galaxies, you will not find another.

Human history can be viewed as a slowly dawning awareness that we are members of a larger group. Initially, our loyalties were to ourselves and to our immediate family. Next, our loyalty was to bands of wandering hunter-gatherers; then to tribes, small settle-

"Our loyalties must . . . include the entire planet Earth."

ments, states and nations. We have broadened the circle of those we love.

If we are to survive, our loyalties must be broadened further to include the whole human community, the entire planet Earth.

A CLOSER LOOK

1. According to Sagan, why do some people fear or distrust those who are different from them? Does Sagan think this attitude is changing? Why or why not?

2. Would extraterrestrial visitors care about the differences among human beings? Why or why not?

3. What changes in human behavior do you think Sagan would like to see? What changes would you like to see?

"Tommy: They looked just like humans."

Rod Serling

THE MONSTERS ARE DUE ON MAPLE STREET

● If creatures from another planet landed on Earth, how would you react? In this play, Serling takes a hard look into the human heart to see how we might greet our interplanetary visitors.

CAST

NARRATOR	TOMMY
LES GOODMAN	SALLY
MRS. GOODMAN	MAN
DON MARTIN	SECOND MAN
STEVE BRAND	WOMAN
MRS. BRAND	FIVE DIFFERENT VOICES
PETE VAN HORN	FIRST FIGURE
CHARLIE	SECOND FIGURE

ACT I

It is a quiet, tree-lined, residential street in a typical American town. The houses have front porches where people sit and swing on gliders, talking to each other across their lawns. STEVE BRAND polishes his car parked in front of his house. His neighbor, DON

MARTIN, *leans against the fender, watching him. A Good Humor man rides a bicycle and is just in the process of stopping to sell some ice cream to a couple of kids. Two women gossip on the front lawn. Another man waters his lawn.*

Narrator: Maple Street, U.S.A., late summer. A tree-lined little world of front porch gliders, hopscotch, the laughter of children, and the bell of an ice cream vendor. At the sound of the roar and the flash of the light, it will be precisely six-forty-three p.m. on Maple Street.

(*At this moment one of the boys,* TOMMY, *looks up and listens to the sound of a tremendous screeching roar from overhead. A flash of light plays on his face, then moves down the street past lawns and porches and rooftops, and then disappears.* STEVE BRAND, *the man who has been polishing his car, stands there transfixed, staring upwards. He looks at* DON MARTIN, *his neighbor from across the street.*)

Steve: What was that? A meteor?
Don (*nods*): That's what it looked like. I didn't hear any crash, though, did you?
Steve (*shakes his head*): Nope, I didn't hear anything except a roar.
Mrs. Brand (*from her porch*): Steve? What was that?
Steve (*raising his voice and looking toward the porch*): Guess it was a meteor, honey. Came awful close, didn't it?
Mrs. Brand: Too close for my money! Much too close.

(*People stand on their porches, watching and talking in low tones.*)

Narrator: Maple Street. Six-forty-four p.m. on a late September evening. (*a pause*) Maple Street in the last calm and reflective moment . . . before the monsters came!

(*We see a* MAN *screwing a light bulb on a front porch, then getting down off the stool to flick the switch and find that nothing happens. A* MAN *working on an electric power mower plugs in the plug. He flicks the switch of the power mower, on and off, but nothing happens. Through the window of a front porch a* WOM-

AN *is seen dialing her phone. Her voice is distant but repetitive.)*

Woman: Operator, operator, something's wrong on the phone, operator!

(MRS. BRAND *comes out on the porch and calls to* STEVE.)

Mrs. Brand *(calling):* Steve, the power's off. I had the soup on the stove, and the stove just stopped working.
Woman: Same thing over here. I can't get anybody on the phone either. The phone seems to be dead.
First Voice: Electricity's off.
Second Voice: Phone won't work.
Third Voice: Can't get a thing on the radio.
Fourth Voice: My power mower won't move, won't work at all.
Fifth Voice: Radio's gone dead!

(PETE VAN HORN, *a tall, thin man, is seen standing in front of his house.)*

Van Horn: I'll cut through the back yard . . . see if the power's still on on Floral Street. I'll be right back!
Steve: Doesn't make sense. Why should the power go off all of a sudden *and* the phone line?
Don: Maybe some kind of an electrical storm or something.
Charlie: That don't seem likely. Sky's just as blue as anything. Not a cloud. No lightning. No thunder. No nothing. How could it be a storm?
Woman: I can't get a thing on the radio. Not even the portable.
Charlie: Well, why don't you go downtown and check with the police, though they'll probably think we're crazy or something. A little power failure and right away we get all flustered and every-thing —
Steve: It isn't just the power failure, Charlie. If it was, we'd still be able to get a broadcast on the portable.

(There's a murmur of reaction to this. STEVE *looks from face to face and then over to his car.)*

Steve: I'll run downtown. We'll get this all straightened out.

"Narrator: Maple Street . . . before the monsters came."

(STEVE *walks over to the car, gets into it, turns the key. The engine starts. It turns over sluggishly, and then just stops dead. He tries it again, and this time he can't get it to turn over. Then very slowly and reflectively he turns the key back to "off" and then gets out of the car. He stands for a moment by the car and then walks toward the group.)*

Steve: I don't understand it. It was working fine before —
Don: Out of gas?
Steve *(shakes his head)*: I just had it filled up.
Woman: What's it mean?
Charlie: It's just as if . . . as if everything had stopped. *(Then he turns toward* STEVE.*)* We'd better walk downtown.

(There is another murmur of assent to this.)

Steve: Two of us can go, Charlie. *(He turns to look back at the car.)* It couldn't be the meteor. A meteor couldn't do *this.*

(He and CHARLIE *exchange a look. Then they start to walk away*

170

from the group. TOMMY, *a serious-faced young boy in spectacles, stands a few feet away from the group, halfway between them and the two men who start to walk down the sidewalk.*)

Tommy: Mr. Brand . . . you'd better not!
Steve: Why not?
Tommy: They don't want you to.

(STEVE *and* CHARLIE *exchange a grin.* STEVE *looks back toward the boy.*)

Steve: *Who* doesn't want us to?
Tommy (*jerks his head in the general direction of the distant horizon*): Them!
Steve: Them?
Charlie: Who are them?
Tommy (*very intently*): Whoever was in that thing that came by overhead.
Steve: What?
Tommy: Whoever was in that thing that came over. I don't think they want us to leave here.

(STEVE *leaves* CHARLIE *and walks over to the boy. He kneels down in front of him. He forces his voice to remain gentle. He reaches out and holds the boy.*)

Steve: What do you mean? What are you talking about?
Tommy: They don't want us to leave. That's why they shut everything off.
Steve: What makes you say that? Whatever gave you *that* idea?
Woman (*from the crowd*): Now isn't that the craziest thing you ever heard?
Tommy (*persistently*): It's always that way, in every story I ever read about a ship landing from outer space.
Woman (*to the boy's mother,* SALLY, *who stands on the fringe of the crowd*): From outer space yet! Sally, you better get that boy of yours up to bed. He's been reading too many comic books or seeing too many movies or something!
Sally: Tommy, come over here and stop that kind of talk.
Steve: Go ahead, Tommy. We'll be right back. And you'll see. That

wasn't any ship or anything like it. That was just a . . . a meteor or something. Likely as not — *(He turns to the group, now trying to weight his words with an optimism he obviously doesn't feel but is desperately trying to instill in himself as well as in the others.)* No doubt it did have something to do with all this power failure and the rest of it. Meteors can do some crazy things. Like sun spots.

Don *(picking up the cue)*: Sure. That's the kind of thing — like sun spots. They raise Cain with radio reception all over the world. And this thing, being so close — why, there's no telling the sort of stuff it can do. *(He wets his lips, smiles nervously.)* Go ahead, Charlie. You and Steve go into town and see if that isn't what's causing it all.

(STEVE and CHARLIE again continue to walk away from the group down the sidewalk. The people watch silently. TOMMY stares at them, biting his lips and finally calling out again.)

Tommy: Mr. Brand!

(The two men stop again. TOMMY takes a step toward them.)

Tommy: Mr. Brand . . . please don't leave here.

(STEVE and CHARLIE stop once again and turn toward the boy. There's a murmur in the crowd, a murmur of irritation and concern, as if the boy were bringing up fears that shouldn't be brought up.)

Tommy: You might not even be able to get to town. It was that way in the story. *Nobody* could leave. Nobody except —
Steve: Except who?
Tommy: Except the people they'd sent down ahead of them. They looked just like humans. And it wasn't until the ship landed that — *(The boy suddenly stops again, conscious of his parents staring at him and of the sudden hush of the crowd.)*
Sally *(in a whisper, sensing the antagonism of the crowd)*: Tommy, please, son . . . honey, don't talk that way —
Man: The kid shouldn't talk that way . . . and we shouldn't stand here listening to him. Why, this is the craziest thing I ever heard

172

of. The kid tells us a comic-book plot, and here we stand listening —

(STEVE walks toward the boy.)

Steve: Go ahead, Tommy. What kind of story was this? What about
the people that they sent out ahead?
Tommy: That was the way they prepared things for the landing.
They sent four people. A mother and a father and two kids who
looked just like humans . . . but they weren't.

*(There's laughter at this, but it's a laughter that comes from a
desperate attempt to lighten the atmosphere. It's a release kind of
laugh. The people look at one another in the middle of their
laughter.)*

Charlie *(rubs his jaw nervously)*: I wonder if Floral Street's got the
same deal we got. *(He looks past the houses.)* Where is Pete Van
Horn, anyway? Didn't he get back yet?

*(Suddenly there's the sound of a car's engine starting to turn over.
LES GOODMAN is at the wheel of his car.)*

Sally: Can you get started, Les?

(GOODMAN gets out of the car, shaking his head.)

Goodman: No dice.

*(As he walks toward the group, he stops suddenly. Behind him,
the car engine starts up all by itself. GOODMAN whirls around
and stares at it. The car idles roughly. Smoke comes from the
exhaust, and the frame shakes gently. GOODMAN's eyes go
wide, and he runs over to his car. The people stare toward the
car.)*

Man: He got the car started somehow. He got *his* car started!
Woman: How come his car just up and started like that?
Sally: All by itself. He wasn't anywhere near it. It started all by
itself.

(DON approaches the group. He stops a few feet away to look toward Goodman's car and then back toward the group.)

Don: And he never did come out to look at that thing that flew overhead. He wasn't even interested. *(He turns to the faces in the group, his own face taut and serious.)* Why? Why didn't he come out with the rest of us to look?

Charlie: He was always an oddball. Him and his whole family. Real oddball.

Don: What do you say we ask him?

(The group suddenly starts toward the house. For a moment their fear almost turns their walk into a wild stampede, but STEVE's voice, loud and commanding, makes them stop.)

Steve: Wait a minute . . . *wait a minute!* Let's not be a mob!

(The people stop as a group, seem to pause for a moment. Then, much more quietly and slowly, they start to walk across the street. GOODMAN stands there alone, facing the people.)

Goodman: I just don't understand it. I tried to start it, and it wouldn't start. You saw me. All of you saw me.

(And now, just as suddenly as the engine started, it stops. There's a frightened murmuring of the people.)

Goodman: I don't understand . . . I don't understand. What's happening?

Don: Maybe you better tell us. Nothing's working on this street. Nothing. No lights, no power, no radio. *(then meaningfully)* Nothing except one car — *yours!*

(The people pick this up, and their murmuring becomes a loud chant filling the air with demands for action. Two of the men pass DON and head toward GOODMAN, who backs away.)

Goodman: Wait a minute now. You keep your distance — all of you. So I've got a car that starts by itself — well, that's a freak thing — I admit it. But does that make me some kind of a

174

criminal or something? I don't know why the car works — it just does!

(This stops the crowd, and GOODMAN, *still backing away, goes toward his front porch. He goes up the steps and then stops to face the mob.)*

Goodman: What's it all about, Steve?

Steve *(quietly)*: We're all on a monster kick, Les. Seems that the general impression holds that maybe the people in one family aren't what we think they are. Monsters from outer space or something. Different than us. Fifth columnists[1] from the vast beyond. *(He chuckles.)* You know anybody that might fit that description around here on Maple Street?

Goodman: What is this, a gag or something? This a practical joke or something?

(Suddenly the engine of the car starts all by itself again, runs for a moment, and stops. The people once again react.)

Goodman: Now that's supposed to incriminate me, huh? The car engine goes on and off, and that really does it, doesn't it? *(He looks around at the faces of the people.)* I just don't understand it . . . any more than any of you do! *(He wets his lips, looking from face to face.)* Look, you all know me. We've lived here five years. Right in this house. We're no different than any of the rest of you! We're no different at all. Really . . . this whole thing is just . . . just weird —

Woman: Well, if that's the case, Les Goodman, explain why — *(She stops suddenly, clamping her mouth shut.)*

Goodman *(softly)*: Explain what?

Steve *(interjecting)*: Look, let's forget this —

Charlie *(overlapping him)*: Go ahead; let her talk. What about it? Explain what?

Woman *(a little reluctantly)*: Well . . . sometimes I go to bed late at night. A couple of times . . . a couple of times I'd come out here on the porch and I'd see Mr. Goodman here in the wee hours of the morning standing out in front of his house . . . looking up at the sky. *(She looks around at the circle of faces.)* That's right, looking up at the sky as if . . . as if he were waiting for something. *(a pause)* As if he were looking for something.

(There's a murmur of reaction from the crowd again. GOODMAN *backs away.)*

Goodman: She's crazy. Look, I can explain that. Please. . . I can really explain that. She's making it up anyway. *(then he shouts)* I tell you, she's making it up!

(He takes a step toward the crowd, and they back away. He walks down the steps after them, and they continue to back away. He's suddenly and completely left alone. He looks like a man caught in the middle of a menacing circle.)

ACT II

Scene One

From the various houses we can see candlelight but no electricity. There's an all-pervading quiet that blankets the whole area, disturbed only by the almost whispered voices of the people as they stand around. CHARLIE *stares across at Goodman's house. Two men stand across the street from it in almost sentry-like poses.*

Sally *(a little timid)*: It doesn't seem right, though, keeping watch on them. Why, he was right when he said he was one of our neighbors. Why, I've known Ethel Goodman ever since they moved in. We've been good friends —

Charlie: That don't prove a thing. Any guy who'd spend his time lookin' up at the sky early in the morning — well, there's something wrong with that kind of person. There's something that ain't legitimate. Maybe under normal circumstances we could let it go by, but these aren't normal circumstances. Why, look at this street! Nothin' but candles. Why, it's like goin' back into the dark ages or somethin'!

(STEVE, from several yards away, walks down the steps of his porch, and down the street over to Les Goodman's house. He stops at the foot of the steps. GOODMAN stands there. MRS.

176

GOODMAN *stands behind him, very frightened.)*

Goodman: Just stay right where you are, Steve. We don't want any trouble, but this time if anybody sets foot on my porch — that's what they're going to get — trouble!

Steve: Look, Les —

Goodman: I've already explained to you people. I don't sleep very well at night sometimes. I get up and I take a walk and I look up at the sky. I look at the stars!

Mrs. Goodman: That's exactly what he does. Why, this whole thing, it's . . . it's some kind of madness or something.

Steve *(nods grimly)*: That's exactly what it is — some kind of madness.

Charlie's voice *(shrill, from across the street)*: You best watch who you're seen with, Steve! Until we get this all straightened out, you ain't exactly above suspicion yourself.

Steve *(whirling around toward him)*: Or you, Charlie. Or any of us, it seems. From age eight and up!

Woman: What I'd like to know is — what are we gonna do? Just stand around here all night?

Charlie: There's nothin' else we *can* do! *(He turns back, looking toward* STEVE *and* GOODMAN *again.)* One of 'em'll tip their hand. They *got* to.

Steve *(raising his voice)*: There's something you can do, Charlie. You could go home and keep your mouth shut. You could quit strutting around like a self-appointed hanging judge and just climb into bed and forget it.

Charlie: You sound real anxious to have that happen, Steve. I think we better keep our eye on you, too!

Don: I think everything might as well come out now. *(He turns toward* STEVE.*)* Your wife's done plenty of talking, Steve, about how odd *you* are!

Charlie *(picking this up, his eyes widening)*: Go ahead, tell us what she's said.

(STEVE *walks toward them from across the street.)*

Steve: Go ahead, what's my wife said? Let's get it *all* out. Let's pick out every idiosyncrasy[2] of every single man, woman, and child on the street. And then we might as well set up some kind of kangaroo court.[3] How about a firing squad at dawn, Charlie, so we can get rid of all the suspects? Narrow them down.

Don: There's no need getting so upset, Steve. It's just that . . . well . . . Myra's talked about how there's been plenty of nights you spent hours down in your basement workin' on some kind of radio or something. Well, none of us have ever *seen* that radio —

(By this time STEVE *has reached the group. He stands there defiantly close to them.)*

Charlie: Go ahead, Steve. What kind of "radio set" you workin' on? I've never seen it. Neither has anyone else. Who do you talk to on the radio set? And who talks to you?

Steve: I'm surprised at you, Charlie. How come you're so dense all of a sudden? *(a pause)* Who do I talk to? I talk to monsters from outer space. I talk to three-headed green men who fly over here in what look like meteors.

*(*MRS. BRAND *steps down from the porch, bites her lip, calls out.)*

Mrs. Brand: Steve! Steve, please. *(Then looking around frightened, she walks toward the group.)* It's just a ham radio set, that's all. I bought him a book on it myself. It's just a ham radio set. A lot of people have them. I can show it to you. It's right down in the basement.

Steve *(whirls around toward her)*: Show them nothing! If they want to look inside our house — let them get a search warrant.

Charlie: Look, buddy, you can't afford to —

Steve *(interrupting)*: Charlie, don't start telling me who's dangerous and who isn't, and who's safe and who's a menace. *(He turns to the group and shouts.)* And you're with him, too — all of you! You're standing here all set to crucify — all set to find a scapegoat[4] — all desperate to point some kind of a finger at a neighbor! Well now, look, friends, the only thing that's gonna happen is that we'll eat each other up alive —

(He stops abruptly as CHARLIE *suddenly grabs his arm.)*

178

Charlie *(in a hushed voice)*: That's not the *only* thing that can happen to us.
(A figure suddenly materializes in the gloom. In the silence we can hear the clickety-clack of slow, measured footsteps on concrete as the figure walks slowly toward them. One of the women lets out a stifled cry.)

Tommy *(shouting, frightened)*: It's the monster! It's the monster!

(Another woman lets out a wail. The people fall back in a group, staring toward the darkness and the approaching figure. DON MARTIN joins them, carrying a shotgun. He holds it up.)

Don: We may need this.
Steve: A shotgun? *(He pulls it out of DON's hand.)* Will anybody think a thought around here? Will you people wise up? What good would a shotgun do against —

(CHARLIE pulls the gun from STEVE's hand.)

Charlie: No more talk, Steve. You're going to talk us into a grave! You'd let whatever's out there walk right over us, wouldn't yuh? Well, some of us won't!

(He swings the gun around to point it toward the sidewalk. The dark figure continues to walk toward them. CHARLIE slowly raises the gun. As the figure gets closer, he pulls the trigger. The sound explodes in the stillness. The figure lets out a small cry, stumbles forward onto his knees, and then falls forward on his face. DON, CHARLIE, and STEVE race forward over to him. STEVE is there first and turns the man over. The crowd gathers around them.)

Steve *(slowly looks up)*: It's Pete Van Horn.
Don *(in a hushed voice)*: Pete Van Horn! He was just gonna go over to the next block to see if the power was on —
Woman: You killed him, Charlie. You shot him dead!
Charlie *(looks around at the circle of faces, his eyes frightened, his face contorted)*: But . . . but I didn't know who he was. I certain-

ly didn't know who he was. He comes walkin' out of the darkness — how am I supposed to know who he was? *(He grabs STEVE.)* Steve — you know why I shot! How was I supposed to know he wasn't a monster or something? *(He grabs DON.)* We're all scared of the same thing. I was just tryin' to . . . tryin' to protect my home, that's all! Look, all of you, that's all I was tryin' to do. *(He looks down wildly at the body.)* I didn't know it was somebody we knew! I didn't know —

(There's a sudden hush and then an intake of breath in the group. Across the street all the lights go on in one of the houses.)

Woman *(in a very hushed voice)*: Charlie . . . Charlie . . . the lights just went on in your house. Why did the lights go on?
Don: What about it, Charlie? How come you're the only one with lights now?
Goodman: That's what I'd like to know.

(There's a pause as they all stare toward CHARLIE.)

Goodman: You were so quick to kill, Charlie, and you were so quick to tell us who we had to be careful of. Well, maybe you *had* to kill. Maybe Pete there was trying to tell us something. Maybe he'd found out something and came back to tell us who there was amongst us we should watch out for —

(CHARLIE backs away from the group, his eyes wide with fright.)

Charlie: No . . . no . . . it's nothing of the sort! I don't know why the lights are on. I swear I don't. Somebody's pulling a gag or something.

(He bumps against STEVE, who grabs him and whirls him around.)

Steve: A gag? *A gag?* Charlie, there's a dead man on the sidewalk, and you killed him! Does this thing look like a gag to you?

(CHARLIE breaks away and screams as he runs toward his house.)

"First Figure: Their world is full of Maple Streets."

Charlie: No! No! Please!

(A man breaks away from the crowd to chase CHARLIE. *The man tackles him and lands on top of him. The other people start to run toward them.* CHARLIE *gets up on his feet, breaks away from the other man's grasp, and lands a couple of desperate punches that push the man aside. Then he forces his way, fighting, through the crowd. He once again breaks free and jumps up on his front porch. A rock thrown from the group smashes a window alongside of him. The broken glass flies past him. A couple of pieces cut him. He stands there perspiring, rumpled, blood running down from a cut on his cheek. His wife breaks away from the group and throws herself into his arms. He buries his face against her. We can see the crowd converging on the porch.)*

First Voice: It must have been him.
Second Voice: He's the one.
Third Voice: We've got to get Charlie.

(Another rock lands on the porch. CHARLIE *pushes his wife*

behind him and faces the group.)

Charlie: Look, look, I swear to you . . . it isn't me . . . but I do know who it is. I swear to you, I do know who it is. I know who the monster is here. I know who it is that doesn't belong. I swear to you I know.

Don *(pushing his way to the front of the crowd)*: All right, Charlie, let's hear it!

Second Man *(screaming)*: Go ahead, Charlie; tell us.

Charlie: It's . . . it's the kid. It's Tommy. He's the one!

Sally *(backs away)*: That's crazy. That's crazy. He's only a boy.

Woman: But he knew! He was the only one who knew! He told us all about it. Well, how did he know? How *could* he have known?

(People in the crowd take this up and repeat the question aloud.)

First Voice: How could he know?
Second Voice: Who told him?
Third Voice: Make the kid answer.

(The crowd starts to converge around the mother, who grabs TOMMY and starts to run with him. The crowd starts to follow, at first walking fast, and then running after SALLY and TOMMY. Suddenly CHARLIE's lights go off, and the lights in another house go on. They stay on for a moment, and then from across the street other lights go on and then off again.)

Man *(shouting)*: It isn't the kid . . . it's Bob Weaver's house.
Woman: It isn't Bob Weaver's house; it's Don Martin's place.
Charlie: I tell you it's the kid.
Don: It's Charlie. He's the one.

(Various people shout, accuse each other, scream. House lights go on and off.)

Scene Two
In a nearby field a space craft sits shrouded in darkness. An open door throws out a beam of light from the illuminated interior. Two figures silhouetted against the bright lights appear.

First Figure: Understand the procedure now? Just stop a few of their machines and radios and telephones and lawn mowers . . . throw them into darkness for a few hours, and then just sit back and watch the pattern.

Second Figure: And this pattern is always the same?

First Figure: With few variations. They pick the most dangerous enemy they can find . . . and it's themselves. And all we need to do is sit back . . . and watch.

Second Figure: Then I take it this place . . . this Maple Street . . . is not unique.

First Figure (*shaking his head*): By no means. Their world is full of Maple Streets. And we'll go from one to the other and let them destroy themselves. One to the other . . . one to the other . . . one to the other —

Scene Three

We see the starry sky and hear the NARRATOR'*s voice.*

Narrator: The tools of conquest do not necessarily come with bombs and explosions and fallout. There are weapons that are simply thoughts, attitudes, prejudices — to be found only in the minds of men and women. For the record, prejudices can kill and suspicion can destroy, and a thoughtless, frightened search for a scapegoat has a fallout all of its own for the children . . . and the children yet unborn.

---

[1] **fifth columnists:** secret supporters of the enemy
[2] **idiosyncrasy:** a habit, thought to be unusual
[3] **kangaroo court:** a court in which the principles of law are disregarded or distorted
[4] **scapegoat:** an innocent person who bears the blame for others

A CLOSER LOOK

1. How does the panic begin? Why does it increase?

2. Briefly describe the personality of three of the characters in this play. How do you think Serling feels about them?

3. Why do you think Serling set this play in a typical small town? Do you think an incident like this could happen where you live? Why or why not?

James Thurber
THE LAST FLOWER

● Humorist James Thurber called this fable "A Parable in Pictures."
A parable is a moral lesson turned into a short story in order to
make it more interesting and convincing. The lesson, you'll agree, is
as important today as when Thurber wrote "The Last Flower" in the
opening years of World War Two.

A CLOSER LOOK

1. At the beginning of the story, what has disappeared from the Earth? Why?

2. What causes civilization to be reborn? At what point do you think it begins to go downhill again? What human trait(s) do you think Thurber is criticizing?

3. What do you think is going to happen after the last drawing in the story? Do you think this vision of the future is hopeful or gloomy?